The Virginia ATCHLEY

Collection of
Japanese Miniature Arts

The Virginia ATCHLEY

Collection of Japanese Miniature Arts

by Virginia Atchley and Neil Davey

Acknowledgements

We are greatly indebted to several people who have worked on or supported the publication of the Virginia Atchley collection.

Virginia's husband Raymond and Neil's wife Sue have given much support throughout and Sue has assisted greatly in the preparation of the indices of artists, publications and exhibitions.

Virginia's daughter, Susan has given much support from the conception of the project.

We wholeheartedly thank Hollis Goodall of the Los Angeles County Museum of Art for her wonderful introductory essay.

We also thank Chris Drosse of the same museum for compiling the glossary of terms and the subject index.

We are grateful to Susan Einstein for her photographic expertise in a notoriously difficult field.

Patricia G. McConnell has done an excellent job of copy editing the text and any remaining errors are solely down to Neil Davey.

Heinz and Else Kress, as well as Sebastian Izzard were very helpful in elucidating certain subjects.

Finally, Rosanne and Tony Chan of CA Design have been patient for many months and we are delighted with the design that they have produced.

Virginia Atchley and Neil Davey

Catalogue by Virginia Atchley and Neil Davey

Designed by Rosanne Chan
Produced by C A Design, Hong Kong

ISBN 1-58886-086-8

Contents

Preface

Netsuke, inro, pipe-cases and "related accoutrements" are miniature forms of Japanese art that have enriched and gladdened my life ever since, in 1963, I discovered and bought my first netsuke during a visit to my home town of Boston. It was a small seated wood rat, with inlaid horn eyes, and the dealer, Mr. Yatsuhashi, told me that it was signed Ikkan, a famous carver from Nagoya in the 19th century. The price was $80 which, at the time, seemed like a lot of money to me. "But just once," I told myself, quite unaware of what a Pandora's box I was opening.

Having once yielded to temptation, I soon bought another netsuke in a local gallery. Then my husband, Raymond, brought two more back from a business trip to San Francisco. My daughter, Susan, was also enthusiastic. I subscribed to Sotheby's and Christie's catalogues of Japanese art. Thus a small beginning, with loyal family support, grew like Topsy into what became a considerable collection.

For my own satisfaction, and with a desire to share with other collectors what has given me so much pleasure over the years, I am happy to add this volume to others in the field.

Virginia Atchley

The Fashion for *Sagemono* in Edo Japan (1615–1868)

Hollis Goodall

Aesthetics and self-identity were closely interrelated concepts in Japan from early in its recorded history. The first novel, *The Tale of Genji*, written in the 11th century, is replete with indications that a person's worth was measured by his or her skills in poetry and calligraphy, in connoisseurship of painting, in the design of gardens, and, central to this discussion, in the tastefulness of the manner of dress. Each of these attributes or accomplishments is equally important to the aesthetics of *sagemono* (suspended objects), from the time they were first used in the 16th century until their demise in the 20th century.

Sagemono, which were suspended from a man's waist sash (*obi*), generally consisted largely of tobacco pouches (*tabako-ire*), hard-cased tobacco containers (*tonkotsu*), money purses (*kinchaku*), flint pouches (*hiuchibukuro*) and, most precious of all, medicine or "seal containers", called *inro*. Common counter-weights or toggles, used to hold the container in place on the obi, were *netsuke* ("root attachment") or pipe cases (*kiseruzutsu*). The pipe cases held pipes averaging 7 to 9 inches in length. (Other pipes for non-portable use could be any size.)

Although Japanese garment ensembles lacked pockets, they had sleeves that could hold small objects or papers, the aforementioned obi from which containers could be suspended and, especially in women's *kimono*, a protected fold where fabric crosses at the chest, into which small containers, pipes or other objects could be secreted.

Samurai needed to carry weapons at their waist, leaving their hands free to tend to a horse, hold battle accoutrements or be ready for defense. Hunters also habitually carried flint pouches, knives or other tools at the waist. Sagemono came to be used by the general populace with the introduction and dissemination of medicines from the Chinese, tobacco from the Portuguese and standardised coinage minted in Japan in the early 17th century, after the country was united following a century of war (c. 1467–1568).

The most influential advocate of Chinese medicines was the first *shogun* of the Edo period (1615–1868), Tokugawa Ieyasu (1543–1616). His fascination with pharmacopoeias had a wide-ranging influence; by the mid-seventeenth century, men of means, often samurai, carried elixirs in their layered lacquer inro. One of Tokugawa Ieyasu's inro is in the collection of the Tokugawa Museum in Nagoya. **[fn1]** The history and development of inro has been discussed so eloquently and thoroughly elsewhere that it is unnecessary to repeat it here. **[fn 2]**

Tobacco and its accessories have been less comprehensively described in English. **[fn 3]** No documents exist to give a precise date for the entry of tobacco into Japan, though its importation and dissemination are known to have occurred between about 1543 and 1600, when Japan traded with Portugal. As an imported product, tobacco was both expensive and coveted; it was also valued for its perceived medicinal properties. By the beginning of the Edo period, farmers were planting tobacco, as yet a non-taxable farm product, to supplement their incomes. As farmers substituted tobacco for rice in their fields, the government saw imminent danger of a lack of both sustenance and taxable resources for the samurai class; therefore at various intervals during the seventeenth century, growing and smoking tobacco were declared illegal. Genre paintings from the 17th century show either *kabuki-mono* (perhaps best defined as "brash youths") smoking at parties under the cherry blossoms or maple leaves, young samurai with courtesans or youthful male entertainers smoking in private interior settings. Tobacco use is never seen in a public or "official" context.

Smoking utensils of the 17th century differ dramatically from their later counterparts, seen in the Virginia Atchley collection. The pipes carried by the Portuguese, depicted in the so-called Namban (southern barbarian) folding screens, and those carried by fashionable Japanese men and women in 17th century genre screens are long, ranging up to about one metre in length, with a fairly sizeable bowl for tobacco at the end of a "goose-neck" stem. It appears from these paintings that samurai and courtesans would never carry their own pipe; rather, it would be toted and prepared by a servant or *kamuro* (young courtesan in training). Part of the reason for the excessive length of the pipe was

the harshness of the imported tobacco's taste, which was evidently ameliorated by the distance of the source of the fire from the mouth. During the late 17th and 18th centuries, when the Japanese were again allowed to grow, process and distribute tobacco for the market, the tobacco was refined into a form which was more easily smoked. This later tobacco is visually striking for its hair-fine strands, a small cluster of which could be inserted into a tiny pipe bowl and smoked through a much shorter pipe. Shorter pipes, in turn, had the distinct advantage of being highly portable.

In the 18th and 19th centuries, these shorter pipes (*kiseru*) became fashionable accessories for affluent merchants and artisans who were at the low end of the "samurai, farmer, artisan, merchant" class system. Visible evidence of class distinction was maintained through sumptuary laws asserting that samurai could and should wear luxury articles, such as purple- or red-dyed silks, and could own and display objects made with gold or precious stones. Merchants, diminished in the social order for their perceived dependence on the other classes, were limited to wearing cotton and ramie coloured with less expensive dyes; however, people of the merchant class are often shown in prints and genre paintings wearing red-dyed undergarments, which could be hidden from the view of passing officials. Small portable accessories were not regulated by these laws and so became for all classes a way of displaying wealth, literacy or worldly knowledge, connoisseurship of fine craft, and awareness of fashion.

The tasteful assemblage of, for example, a pipe case, *ojime* (slide bead) and tobacco pouch was more important than the individual parts. While modern collectors have devoted tremendous attention to individual netsuke or inro, during the Edo period the combination of these elements defined the wearer's taste. Mrs. Atchley has a clear sense for the objects' original intent, and she has developed an eye for the ensemble that can be seen in the humorous pairing of a netsuke of the god of thunder (called Kaminari, Raijin or Raiden), with an inro

showing a scene of porters being scared witless by a
lightning bolt. [**IN 49**] Similarly droll is her pairing of an inro
decorated with a scattering of kites, including a large kite
with the face of Daruma (Bodhidharma, who brought Zen
from India to China), with a netsuke carved as the mask of
an Usofuki character from a *kyogen* play — one who blows
out lies — here apparently using his breath to keep the

kites aloft. [**IN 61**] Both ensembles convey Mrs. Atchley's wit, taste and
knowledge of the subject, as well as her resourcefulness in finding the
appropriate objects to combine. A similar display of discrimination, knowledge
and humour would have been the goal of the first wearer of such sagemono.

Accessory groupings in turn complemented
the overall garment ensemble and, within
the broad fashion trends for clothing,
we see a simultaneous evolution in
sagemono. During the Momoyama period
(1573–1615), when sagemono began to
proliferate, styles in painting, lacquer
decoration and costume followed a
singular path toward exuberance. Grounds
of gold dominated in screen painting and
lacquer, along with bold, heavily pigmented motifs. Motifs were often black, gold,
green, blue and red on screen and sliding door paintings, with black, gold and red
fulfilling a similar role in lacquer. Fabrics for clothing also had large-scale motifs
and, again, zones of black or dark blue and red were used either for background
or for large patterns, often with white as the balancing colour. Rather than
mimicking the broad gold areas of screen paintings or lacquers on flexible cloth,
details were created with gold thread.

Bold patterns were considered desirable on more sizeable writing boxes or on
kimono, against which the tightly detailed gold and black patterning of small
boxes and bags served as a point of contrast. In overall tone, inro produced in the
16th or 17th centuries are relatively subdued or monochromatic, but their use of
gold and black lacquers, with flashes of occasional colour, is rich and elegant. One
inro in the Atchley collection features chrysanthemums in relief (*takamakie*), with

some of the flowers composed of tiny, thin pieces of shell (*aogai*). When new, this inro would have been mostly gold with shell highlights; now, after centuries of wear, the dark under layers of lacquer show through. [**IN 1**] An inro such as this would clearly demand careful examination, especially when seen against a garment having large patterns. Similarly, an inro with a dragon traversing multiple cloud layers over a background of low-relief waves requires tight scrutiny to be viewed properly. [**IN 3**] On each of these inro,

motifs are exquisite in their fine detail and execution. Juxtaposition of large to small pattern, and the interest of examining tiny, delightful objects, defines the aesthetic role of inro at this point. [**Fn 4**]

Like inro, which played a role in aesthetics by providing elegance through contrast, early tabako-ire assumed more than one design function. They, too, were distinctive, and frequently dark in tone. Because they were often made from rare imported animal skin, smoke-dyed deerskin, or tapestry, brocade or another heavily-textured material, both their surface quality and colour would be prominent against the kimono. [**S57; S59; S60**] In addition to the contrast of silk

or soft cotton kimono fabric against rougher textiles or hide, there was a love of the exotic that engendered a demand for brighter, more visually striking imported materials. *Sarasa*, fancy dyed cotton fabric from India and Southeast Asia, was made into kimono, and its boldly patterned borders used to craft tabako-ire. [**S62**] Wall coverings of stamped and coloured leather made in Holland were prized in Japan; they were often used for tabako-ire, as well as for detail work on various accoutrements for men. [**S64; S58**] Dyed and worked leather and pelts as well as imported fabrics remained popular as material for tabako-ire throughout the Edo period, and their exotic nature made them key to cosmopolitan fashion, allowing these pouches to maintain favour as other fashions changed.

Women used tabako-ire as well, although they inserted tabako-ire into the kimono fabric folded across their breast, rather than suspending them from the obi. Imported fabrics, including sarasa and cut velvet, are frequently found on women's tabako-ire. Light-colored brocaded silk fabric with silver- and gold-wrapped threads made an elegant covering for women's tabako-ire, especially those used by wives of samurai.

Metal fittings (*kanagu*) could be found on the front flap of both men's and women's tabako-ire. Kanagu were made by the same artisans who created sword fittings (for example, *menuki, fuchi* or *kashira*), and their skill was at the high level expected by samurai patrons. Some of these fittings were exquisitely crafted, and sculpted with references to poetry or the seasons, to characters from well-known legends or folk tales, or to humorous or erotic scenes. The plate on the inside of a pouch could cleverly extend and embellish a story or scene that had begun on the fitting. The kanagu, in turn, could dictate theme or colouration for the ojime and

pipe case that would complete the ensemble. One example in the Atchley collection shows a kanagu of a fish-head and holly arrangement, as demon dispellers for the lunar New Year, along with a pipe case decorated with Otafuku (or Okame) and a demon. Together these represent the phrase, *"oni wa soto, fuku wa uchi"* (out with the demons, in with good fortune). [**S63**] Tonkotsu, suspended tobacco containers made of hard materials, were originally intended for outdoor use, to protect tobacco from the elements as it was carried by samurai training in the field, or by hunters, farmers or labourers. Townsmen of the artisan and merchant classes adopted the rural tonkotsu for urban use, giving the containers a new stylistic function through elaborate carving and designs that could convey the wearer's personal taste. Like tabako-ire, the wood, stag antler and other coarse material chosen to fabricate tonkotsu stood out distinctly against a finely woven garment, and would attract the eye. [S81] The tonkotsu's rougher materials and their potential for overall carving meant that the designs were more expressive and sometimes less elegant than those of tabako-ire, the unusual fabric and fine metal fittings of which made them a likely choice for polite gatherings.

One's class or place in society could affect the type of sagemono (especially inro, pipe cases and pipes) that one would carry. Samurai, for example, showed a predilection for lacquer carved in the Chinese manner [**IN 82**] or for exceptionally fine *makie* lacquer (lacquer decorated with sprinkled gold), with designs suited to the samurai's station. [**IN 54**]

Carved red, green and black lacquer trays, containers and vessels from China, admired by samurai and tea masters for their beauty, deep colour and craftsmanship, as well as for their association with the Chinese empire, were imported in great numbers

in the 15th and 16th centuries. China was deeply revered by the leaders of Japan. Not only was it the source of Japan's writing and governing systems and of the Confucian educational system later employed by the Tokugawa shogunate, but its philosophers, poets, artists and warriors were also profoundly influential. In fact, Chinese styles and themes were used in the public rooms of castles and samurai residences to help convey an impression of the samurai's legitimacy as governors. The painstaking craftsmanship of Chinese lacquer, seen in the numerous layers of yellow, green, red and black lacquer that were carved through with designs, were first objects of wonder, and then inspiration for some Japanese lacquerers. Most Japanese artists emulating carved lacquer used the Kamakura-*bori* technique of lacquering over carved wood, or the *tsuikin* method, developed in the Ryukyu Kingdom (now Okinawa), of mixing lacquer with clay, cutting the flattened mixture into designs and affixing them to a lacquered body. Very few craftsmen were privy to the secrets of the original Chinese lacquer techniques, and little is known of Japanese artists who mastered them before the 19th century. The majority of so-called carved lacquer (*tsuishu* or *tsuikoku*) inro made for samurai are, in fact, Kamakura-bori or tsuikin. Themes depicted on these inro reflect traditional Chinese subjects, such as dragons and tigers, ancient worthies [**IN 81**], *guri* cloud patterns or flowers, all of which were deemed appropriate subject matter for the decoration of samurai homes and personal effects. In the residence, as mentioned above, Chinese-style items dominated the public rooms, while Japanese-style decor filled the private quarters. This tendency may have had an equivalent in dress, with Chinese-style accessories being worn for more official occasions, while those of Japanese-style ones were reserved for private gatherings.

Inro composed with spectacular makie effects expressed the samurai's native-style aesthetic. Themes flaunting the samurai's level of erudition — for instance, exquisite floral motifs or courtly scenes that refer to ancient poetry and anecdotes, or animals symbolising loyalty, strength and heroism, which were mainstays of the samurai code of ethics — lead the group of subjects depicted in

makie for samurai consumption. [**IN 42**; **IN 53**] The same principles applied to samurai pipe cases, with extremely elegant makie design or Chinese-style carved lacquer representing samurai taste. [**S 20**; **S 39**] Beautifully carved ivory pipe cases and netsuke were collectible by samurai as well, but were less exclusively intended for their realm. Because samurai were the patrons of noh theatre, it is highly likely that this pipe case with text probably from the *no* play *Saigyozakura* was made for a samurai. [**S13**]

Fashion for inro collected by members of the townsmen class was affected by many factors, including developments in outerwear colouration. Laws changed during the Kyoho era (1716–1736) with the rule of Tokugawa Yoshinobu (r. 1716–1745) who endeavoured to set a new moral standard for both samurai and the general populace in an effort to curb outrageous debt and economic instability. The extravagances of his predecessors had undermined their authority when they had attempted to make reforms; Yoshinobu's self-discipline made his

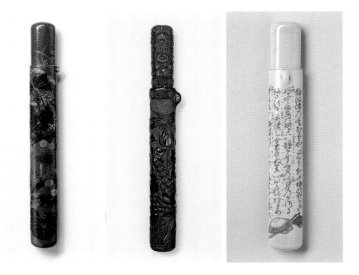

reforms more legitimate to those he ruled. To set an example for the people, he chose to wear garments that had subdued colours and patterns, and he outlawed the use of red- or purple-dyed clothing for those below samurai rank. (He discouraged elaborate clothing for the samurai class as well.) This set Japan on a fresh path in fashion, with a new array of colours developed to replace now-banned red, including a preponderance of subdued tones, especially in men's clothing. In women's clothing, paste-resist (*yuzen*) dye techniques were used to create pictorial effects, replacing the gold details no longer deemed acceptable. Striped or plaid patterns became more prevalent in both men's and women's fashion as colours became more restrained. Sarasa fabrics and other boldly patterned men's clothing disappeared from paintings of this era, as all but the youngest apparently dressed in these quieter tones. One can distinguish the wealthiest men from those in middle or lower economic ranges in these paintings by the relative quality of their kimono cloth, which can be deduced by the drape and flow of their garments. During the late 18th and into the 19th centuries, textiles with grey and brown undertones were most in demand. Olive drab was a color made fashionable by Kabuki actors, whose costume choices often influenced the public. When one wore items in the grey or brown colour range, stylishness was conveyed through carefully chosen contrasting elements, such as undergarments that flashed a different colour (for women), or an inro or tobacco ensemble (for men). The clearest correlation between styles in fabric pattern and colour, and styles of inro, pipe cases, pipes and tabako-ire can be stated as follows: the more subdued the fabric became, the more intricate and elaborate the colouration, inlays and technical treatment of sagemono. [**IN 44; IN 31; IN 78**] Other factors of inro stylistic development evolved from technical advances, a proliferation of artistic schools, and a general progression in the arts toward naturalistic, empirically observed portrayals from nature. However, no matter how much sagemono evolved, a strong impetus remained in place to combine elements with opposing effects.

Like samurai, townsmen had favourite artistic themes and styles that represented their class identity and pride. Designs rendered in Rimpa, literati, and *ukiyo-e* (pictures of the floating world) manners associated with the merchant class might be worn by samurai as well, when they were not asserting their rank; however, to townsmen, these styles signified specific ideas about class. The Rimpa tradition, while not truly a school because it skipped generations between followers of the style, was developed in

Kyoto by Hon'ami Koetsu (1558–1637) and the brilliant painter who worked with him, Tawaraya Sotatsu (?–1643?). The shogunate gave Koetsu a piece of land to the northwest of Kyoto in an area called Takagamine. There, Koetsu organised an artistic and religious commune, separated geographically from the political hotbed in Kyoto, the imperial capital. The style Koetsu and Sotatsu developed (eventually named for their third-generation follower Ogata Korin (1658–1716), using the "rin" from his given name), derived from a new interpretation of paintings produced in the imperial court during its heyday. (10th to 12th centuries). Sotatsu was allowed to view hand scrolls from this era while in the process of repairing them, and he both quoted and updated court themes and aesthetics in his paintings and decorated papers. Koetsu carried these aesthetics into lacquerware. The connection between the Rimpa manner and townsmen derives from its early history. Koetsu and Sotatsu had as their patrons wealthy merchants in Kyoto, whose authority was undermined by the shogun's new class structure, which placed them at the bottom, and whose activities and political power were circumscribed. These merchants showed their dissatisfaction with the shogunate in a way that was unpunishable for its subtlety, by supporting the Rimpa artists' new glorification of court-related arts. The Rimpa style, a radically expressive derivation of true court manner, conveyed the experimental freedom of the Tokugawa era in its early years, but at the same time placed a magnifying glass on the glory of the court, necessarily putting this style in competition with the Chinese-derived manner supported by samurai. This may in part explain why Koetsu and his group were given land so far from town. The samurai devised their

own means of equating their authority with that of the court, including having the shogun formally appointed by the emperor, inter-marrying with princesses, limiting the emperor's decision-making power, and having artists for the shogunate learn a modified court painting manner, named after the main court painter family, the Tosa. By the end of the 18th century, when the Rimpa artist Sakai Hoitsu (1761–1828) gained notoriety, the revolutionary quality of early Rimpa had been diluted; being a Rimpa artist meant following themes from court literature, reinterpreting styles derived from earlier Rimpa masters, and endeavouring to achieve perfect harmony of abstracted forms and mineral colours. [**S 24**] Significantly, Hoitsu was the scion of the

daimyo (feudal lord) of Himeji Castle, and he learned Rimpa style by studying his family's own collection of works by Ogata Korin. This is where the lines blurred between styles preferred by townsmen and those favoured for non-public use by samurai, and why it cannot be said with any certainty which class purchased Rimpa-style inro or pipe cases. Hara Yoyusai (1772-1845) and other inro makers borrowed Hoitsu's designs during the 19th century, bringing his painting style directly into lacquer ware. Rimpa style inro that more closely followed the manner of Koetsu and Korin tended to be boldly designed, often with thick inlays of mother-of-pearl (*raden*) or lead and takamakie against a black or gold ground. [**IN 41**; **IN 8**]

The literati manner developed in response to work of the Kano school, the official painters to the shogunate. Kano artists, or those trained by the school, were responsible for the paintings in meeting rooms of a samurai residence. By the 18th century, this school was so rule-bound that it entirely lost its vitality. Literati, those who cherished and emulated the life and art of the scholar-gentry of China, felt that the connection to China seen in Kano paintings was too diluted to express the genius of that great culture, or to describe the virtues developed through self-instruction in the way demanded by Chinese literati artists. Only by studying the scholar-gentry, their art, character and accomplishments, and by emulating their lifestyle, calligraphy, poetry and music, could one connect with the raw originality and penetration of personal truth achieved by the most skilled among Chinese literati artists and philosophers.

In hierarchical Japanese society, the unfettered nature of Chinese literati, who removed themselves from society and politics, translated into a freedom to move outside the class structure. Like the Chinese, although to a lesser extent, Japanese could improve their station through scholarly achievement. They may not move from townsman to samurai rank, but they could gain more authority within their own station; if they became teachers, they could more freely associate with people above their societal class. In lacquer furnishings and inro, the literati manner is expressed through playful reproduction of the scholar's ink cakes, of scenes of Chinese poets and philosophers or Daoist immortals, and by the depiction of Chinese ideals such as multiple heirs and paragons of filial piety, and symbols of educational progress, such as the determined carp swimming

upstream. [**IN 39**; **IN 28**; **IN 14**] Stones, ceramics or other precious materials could be inlaid in heavily grained wood and then enhanced with lacquer, in a textural manner evocative of the energies of nature. [**IN 7**] While townsmen and samurai shared an interest in literati aesthetics, the scholar's ideal of freedom from rank or political enmeshment and the possibility of bettering one's self and one's social standing through education would have appealed most strongly to the lower classes.

Haiku poetry, as well as satirical *kyoka,* were composed and shared in the licensed pleasure quarters by literati as well as by commercial writers, who sometimes assembled there or in restaurants around town. Haiku aesthetic, as it developed by the late 18th and early 19th centuries, is often expressed in intimate, realistic representations of still-life scenes [**IN 22**; **IN 66**], tea utensils [**IN 30**], garden or floral details, scholars' objects or nature views. As an example of the last, crows on a bare branch poetically express the lonely melancholy of winter. [**IN 52**]

In ukiyo-e, designs often depicted satirical scenes or entertainers and their townsmen customers; it was a way of portraying life outside the limits of the shogun's laws of comportment. People who entered the licensed pleasure quarters, both townsmen and samurai, who disguised themselves to avoid shogunal restrictions against their entry, could happily lose their identity and their concomitant obligations in a place where rank meant nothing and only money and a sense of flair mattered. Poets who met at brothels were recorded under names unrelated to those by which they were known outside the quarter, fostering the impression that they lived an alternate existence in this environment of fantasy. The conspicuous disrespect of the shogunate's laws against profligacy by those escaping to the pleasure quarters as well as the anti-government satire found in so many ukiyo-e images, would indicate that ukiyo-e was specifically a townsman's style. Although it was more likely for townsmen to display a rebellious attitude against the regime that artificially defined their way of living, admiration of theatrical stars, beauties, and sensual pleasure was shared by men of all classes. In the Atchley collection, a relatively old genre design, *tagasode* ("whose sleeves?"), represents a manner that later would evolve into the ukiyo-e style. Kimono are shown draped over a rack, while their owners frolic without them in a space nearby. [**IN 74**] Unlike Rimpa and literati styles, which were practiced nationwide, the ukiyo-e manner was most popular in the largest cities of Edo and Osaka, where theatres were heavily attended and the licensed entertainment quarters had a unique, well-recognised identity.

A final artistic manner, probably equally popular with townsmen and samurai, was the realist style of the Maruyama-Shijo school, which originated in Kyoto at the end of the 18th century. Maruyama Okyo (1733–1795) and his colleague Goshun (1752–1811) combined recently acquired knowledge of Western science with one-point perspective, Japanese traditional compositions and subjects, and a layer of literati poeticism to create a manner that has continued to dominate

Japanese painting in the 19th and 20th centuries. This realistic manner translates best in inro and pipe cases with *togidashi* lacquer, an example of which shows an array of carefully observed, wafting pheasant feathers. [**IN 96**] A new understanding of three-dimensionality, texture, space, mass and light can be seen in these delicately rendered lacquer works.

Acknowledgements:

I would like to thank Virginia Atchley for supporting this project. I would also like to thank Yamakawa Aki, Curator of Costume and Textiles at the Kyoto National Museum, and Sharon Takeda, Curator of Costume and Textiles at the Los Angeles County Museum of Art, for their direction on this essay.

Fn 1. *The Legacy of Tokugawa Ieyasu: Celebrating the 450th Anniversary of the First Shogun* (Nagoya: Tokugawa Art Museum, 1992), p. 117.

Fn 2. Arakawa Hirokazu, *The Go Collection of Netsuke, Tokyo National Museum* (Tokyo and New York: Kodansha International Ltd., 1983); Raymond Bushell, *The Inro Handbook: Studies of Inro, Netsuke and Lacquer* (New York: Weatherhill, 1979); Julia Hutt, *Japanese Inro* (London: Victoria and Albert Museum, 1997); E.A. Wrangham, introduction to Eskenazi, *The Charles A. Greenfield Collection of Japanese Lacquer* (London: 1990), pp. 7–22; E.A. Wrangham, *The Index of Inro Artists* (Alnwick, Northumberland: Harehope Publications, 1995).

Fn 3. Raymond Bushell, "Kiseruzutsu: The Japanese Pipe Case" *Arts of Asia*, vol. 10 no. 6 (1980), 86-95; William and Betty Parker, "The Japanese Personal Smoking Set," *Arts of Asia* vol.13, no. 2 (1983), pp. 94–104; Paul Moss, "Bokko Bokkoku Bokuboku", *International Netsuke Society Journal,* vol. 22, no. 4, (2002), pp. 18–43.

Fn 4. Older samurai, unlike the young set with their broadly designed kimono, would wear indigo-dyed *hakama* covered with small dot patterns. These would be complemented equally by tightly detailed inro.

The netsuke, which form the largest part of the collection, have been categorised by subject matter and, within the various categories, are catalogued more or less chronologically.

Some ancient legendary stories are the subject of ongoing discussion and, in these cases, we have applied our own thoughts in this debate.

It should also be noted that where we feel, as in most signed netsuke, the signature is authentic, we have used the term, "Signed....". When there is doubt, we apply the term "Inscribed....".

Netsuke

N1
Twelve Zodiac Animals
(Junishi)

Ivory, the eyes inlaid
Signed *Kaigyokudo Masatsugu*
(Kaigyokusai Masatsugu)
Osaka, 19th century

Provenance:
F.P. Schneider collection

Kaigyokusai produced a number of Ryusa-style *manju* of similar type, all intricately carved, to represent the twelve animals of the oriental zodiac.

N2
Twelve Zodiac Animals (*Junishi*) on stylised waves

Walnut
Signed *Kozan* (Toryusai Kozan)
Iwashiro, 19th century

Provenance:
F.P. Schneider collection

N3
Rat (*Nezumi*) seated on a gnawed candle

Ivory, the eyes inlaid
Unsigned
Late 18th century

Exhibited:
Los Angeles, November 1977–
February 1978

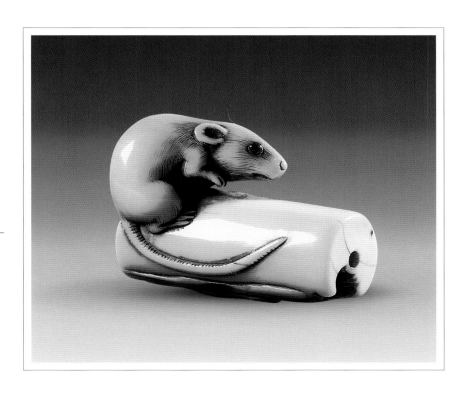

N4
Rat eating a fruit

Wood
Signed in an oval reserve *Tomokazu*
(Kano Tomokazu)
Gifu, early 19th century

N5
Several Rats

Ivory, the eyes inlaid
Inscribed *Tomotada*
Kyoto, 19th century

The rats are playing on the top of a large, well-worn straw hat and carved in fine detail. The work evidently emanates from Kyoto although probably a little later than the signature would indicate.

N6
Rat

Wood
Signed in a rounded rectangular reserve *Ikkan*
Nagoya, 19th century

The rat is seated, playing with a pawn (*keima*) from the game *Shogi no kama*, a chess-like game, played with forty pentagonal-shaped pawns, their names written on each.

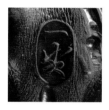

N7
Rat gnawing on a *kuai* bulb

Stag antler
Unsigned, attributed to Ozaki Kokusai
Tokyo, 19th century

Published:
Hurtig, *Masterpieces*, no. 40

Exhibited:
Honolulu, January 1975
Honolulu, January 1977
Minneapolis, September–October 1979

The kuai is a tuberous spring vegetable *(sagittaria sagittata)*.

N8
Recumbent Ox *(Ushi)*

Ivory, the eye pupils inlaid
Inscribed in a rectangular reserve
Tomotada
Kyoto, 18th century

N9
Recumbent Ox

Wood, dark stained, the eyes inlaid with brass
Signed *Kokei*
Tsu, c.1800

Provenance:
Robert Chasin collection

Published:
Chappell and Welch, Netsuke: *The Japanese Art of Miniature Carving*, no. 82
INCS, Vol. 3, no.1, p. 30, fig. 65 and Vol. 9, no. 1, p. 21

Exhibited:
Honolulu, January 1977
Minneapolis, April–July 1998

An unusually large example of Kokei's work, showing the affinity with his master Tanaka Minko.

N10
Tiger *(Tora)*

Boxwood, the eye pupils inlaid
Signed in a rectangular reserve *Tomotada*
(Izumiya Tomotada)
Kyoto, 18th century

Published:
Hurtig, *Masterpieces*, no. 44

Exhibited:
Honolulu, January 1975
Minneapolis, September–October 1979

N11
Tiger and Monkey *(Tora/Saru)*

Ivory, the eye pupils inlaid
Unsigned
Kyoto, 18th century

The work evidently emanates from Kyoto and can be confidently attributed to Mitsuharu, a very similar and signed example having been sold at Sotheby's saleroom in 1966.

N12
Snarling Tiger

Wood
Signed *Kokei*
Tsu, c.1800

Published:
INCS, Vol. 1, no. 4, fig. 3

N13
Toy Tiger

Wood with black lacquered stripes
Unsigned
19th century

Provenance:
Lazarnick collection

Standing on an oval base and with movable head, this is a model of a paper tiger, popular as a child's toy in the Edo period.

N14
Long-eared Hare *(Usagi)*

Boxwood, the eyes inlaid
Unsigned
Late 18th century

Published:
Hurtig, *Masterpieces*, no. 48

Exhibited:
Los Angeles, November 1977–February 1978

N15
Five Rabbits on a Rock

Wood
Signed *Kokei*
Tsu, c.1800

N16
Hare with lespedeza leaves

Ivory and copper
Unsigned
19th century

Of *manju* form, representing the full moon, lightly engraved with a hare nibbling at the leaves, the reverse with a riveted copper plate, leaving an ellipse of ivory, representing the new moon.

N17
Rabbits and Moon

Ivory and *shibuichi kagamibuta*
Unsigned
19th century

Provenance:
Nina McCulloch collection

The *shibuichi* disc bears the design of two rabbits and grasses beneath the misty moon, in gold *takazogan* and *hirazogan* with details of *kebori* engraving.

N18
Rabbits and clouds

Walrus tusk with silver gilt inlay
Signed *Ko*
Edo, late 19th century

N19
Stylised Dragon Head
(Tatsu)

Wood covered with Negoro lacquer, with details of gold lacquered ivory and horn, the eyes of painted crystal
Unsigned
18th century

Provenance:
Albert Brockhaus collection

N20
Dragon

Brass ash tray netsuke
Unsigned
18th century

The dragon is cast in relief on the exterior of the bowl, which bears a loose ring *himotoshi*.

N21
Dragon with *tama* (sacred jewel)

Ivory, the eye pupils inlaid
Unsigned
19th century

N22
Dragon

Solid lacquer and bone
Unsigned
19th century

A solid lacquer *manju*, in layers of red, black, yellow and green, probably formed from the residue left by a lacquerer, once he had finished a larger work. The bone disc is lacquered red and carved in relief with a dragon.

N23
Dragon in clouds

Hirado ware porcelain
Unsigned
19th century

Provenance:
F.P. Schneider collection

Published:
INCS, Vol. 3, no. 2, p. 19, fig. 17

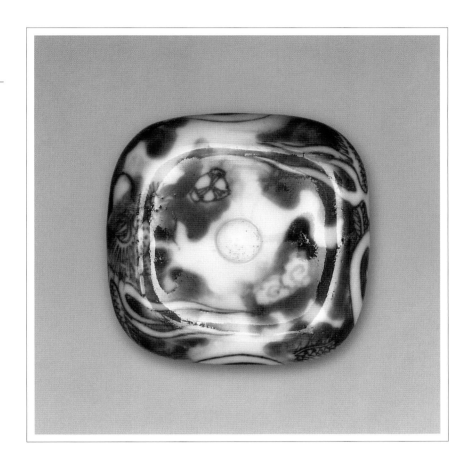

N24
Snake *(Hebi)* and Skull

Bone
Unsigned
19th century

Published:
Hurtig, *Masterpieces*, no. 30

N25
Snake

Wood
Unsigned, style of Shinzan
Masanao
Ise, 20th century

N26
Horse (Uma) and groom

Ivory
Unsigned
Kansai district, 18th century

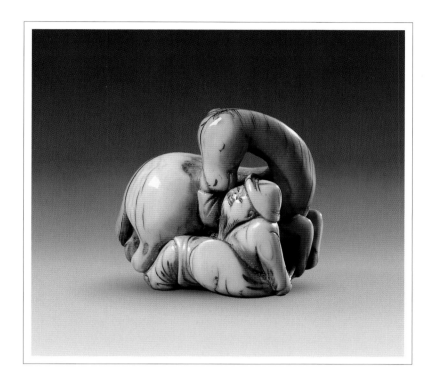

N27
Running Horse

Ivory
Unsigned
Late 18th/early 19th century

The form is eminently suitable for its use as a netsuke, being somewhat flattened and curved.

N28
Recumbent Horse

Ebony
Signed *Kokei*
Tsu, c. 1800

N29
Ojime engraved with a running Horse

Ivory
Signed *Mitsuhiro* with *kakihan*
Osaka, 19th century

N30
Recumbent Horse

Ivory, the eyes of amber with *umimatsu* pupils
Signed and inscribed *Junishi, kazuuchi, Masatsugu* (Kaigyokusai Masatsugu)
Osaka, 19th century

Provenance:
F.P. Schneider collection

Published:
Hurtig, *Masterpieces*, no. 16
Lazarnick, *The Signature Book*, p. 218

This is evidently one of a set of twelve netsuke featuring animals of the oriental zodiac. The inscription reads, "One of the number of twelve zodiac." The style of the signature is that used by Kaigyokusai Masatsugu in his earlier years and could be dated to around 1830.

N31
Horse

Walrus tusk
Signed *LY* (Lee Youngren)
Los Angeles, 20th century

Provenance:
Purchased from the artist

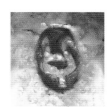

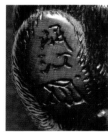

N32
Seated Goat *(Hitsuji)*

Wood, its eyes of brass with dark horn pupils
Signed *Minko* with *kakihan* (Tanaka Minko)
Tsu, Late 18th century

Provenance:
Michael and Rebecca Hauter collection

Published:
Hurtig, *Masterpieces*, no. 310

N33
Monkey *(Saru)*

Stag antler
Unsigned
Probably 17th century

N34
Monkey and Crab

Ivory
Unsigned
18th century

The large crab is pressing down on the grimacing monkey, alluding to the legend *Saru kani kassen* (see also no. N36).

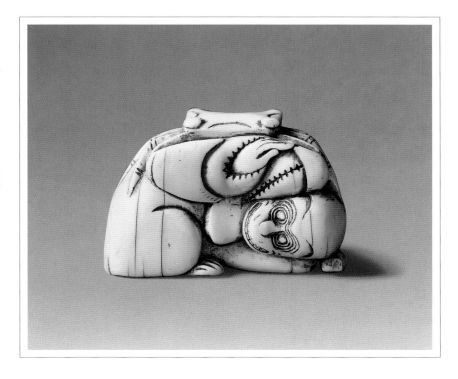

N35
Monkey eating a peach

Wood
Signed *Masatada*
Kyoto, early 19th century

N36
Monkey and Crab

Ivory, the eyes inlaid
Signed *Kaigyoku* (Kaigyokusai
Masatsugu)
Osaka, 19th century

Published:
Chappell and Welch, Netsuke: The *Japanese Art of Miniature Carving*, no. 177
INCS, Vol. 1, no. 4, p. 11, fig. 10

Exhibited:
Honolulu, January 1977
Kansas City, September-November 1977
Minneapolis, September-October 1979
Minneapolis, April–July, 1998

The monkey is taking a rice cake from the crab, an allusion to the legend *Saru kani kassen* (see also no. N34). According to Dr. Richard Wrangham, the monkey is a macaque, of the species *macaca fuscata*, and is an adult male more than eight years old.

N37
Monkey peeling a large fruit

Stag antler
Signed *Koku* (Ozaki Kokusai)
Tokyo, late 19th century

Published:
Hurtig, Masterpieces, no. 19

The signature of Ozaki Kokusai is in typical seal form and is formed by the base. Kokusai was a humorist in his work and often incorporated his simple single character signature in the design of his netsuke.

N38
Cockerel *(Tori)* on a Drum

Wood
Signed *Tomokazu* (Kano Tomokazu)
Gifu, early 19th century

Provenance:
Nina McCullough collection

Published:
Hurtig, *Masterpieces*, no. 46

The subject is symbolic of peace and good governance.

N39
Cockerel and Hen

Wood
Signed *Ryusenshi Issan*
Iwashiro, Early 19th century

Provenance:
Nina McCullough collection

Published:
Hurtig, *Masterpieces*, no. 31

The two fowl are seated together on a folded *tatami* mat with a long inscription beneath, that reads, "Now it is middle autumn. I have to go away. This is given as a present to you."

N40
Bitch *(Inu)* with two Pups

Boxwood
Signed *Kokei*
Tsu, c.1800

Provenance:
W.L. Behrens collection, no. 1641
F. Meinertzhagen collection
J.R. Hawker collection
M.T. Hindson collection

Published:
Davey, *Netsuke*, no. 656
Hurtig, *Masterpieces*, no. 53

N41
Puppies

Ivory
Signed in seal form *Ren* (Ishikawa Rensai)
Tokyo, 19th century

The five puppies, which appear to be similar to German dachshunds, are carved in relief in a sunken panel, while the reverse is carved with a formal flowerhead in relief.

N42
Puppy

Porcelain, blue glazed
Unsigned
Kyushu, 19th century

Provenance:
Hugh Weiser collection

Published:
Hurtig, *Masterpieces*, no. 51

The speckled pale turquoise glaze is derived from the Chinese robin's egg blue *(lü jun)*, prevalent on porcelains of the Qian Long period (1736–1795).

N43
Seated Boar
(I no Shishi)

Boxwood
Signed *Kokei*
Tsu, c. 1800

This netsuke was purchased from a family in Tsu, the birthplace of Kokei, who had owned it for many years.

N44
Sleeping Boar

Wood
Signed *Masakiyo*
Ise, mid to late 19th century

Published:
Hurtig, *Masterpieces*, no. 50
Lazarnick, *The Signature Book*, p. 263

Exhibited:
Honolulu, January 1977
Los Angeles, November 1977–
February 1978

N45
Bat *(Komori)* and Young

Wood
Signed in a sunken oval reserve *Horaku*
Kyoto, 19th century

The bat protects her offspring within the concave form of an old roof tile.

Published:
Chappell and Welch, Netsuke, *The Japanese Art of Miniature Carving*, no. 181

Exhibited:
Minneapolis, April–July, 1998, no. 181

N46
Recumbent Cat (Neko)

Ivory, with three piebald patches inlaid
with horn and with a horn collar and a
mother-of-pearl bell
Unsigned
Late 18th century

Provenance:
M.M. Hepworth collection
M.T. Hindson collection
T. Hahn collection

Published:
Davey, Netsuke, no. 967

N47
Cat and Kitten

Wood
Unsigned
Probably late 18th century

Provenance:
Nina McCullough collection

Published:
Hurtig, *Masterpieces*, no. 10

The cat stands in human attire, holding a kitten
over its shoulder and a large captured rat on a
line. Only one other similar piece is known,
which has been described as the ghost of a cat.

N48
Cat reclining on a rush mat

Narwhal tusk
Unsigned
Early 19th century

Provenance:
Ann Hull Grundy collection

Published:
INCS, Vol. 3, no. 2, p. 19

N49
Wild-cat (Yama-neko)

Boxwood with large inlaid
horn eyes
Signed *Kokei*
Tsu, early 19th century

Published:
Chappell and Welch: *Netsuke, the Japanese Art of Miniature Carving*, no. 92

Exhibited:
Minneapolis, April–July 1998

The style is somewhat removed from that of Kokei, the foremost pupil of Tanaka Minko of Tsu. Also, the signature is engraved in rather large characters, in a rectangular reserve, leading one to suppose that the carver may be another of the same name.

N50
Seated Deer *(Shika)*

Ivory with inlaid eye pupils
Unsigned
Kyoto, 18th century

Provenance:
Fred Rothchild collection

Published:
Hurtig, *Masterpieces*, no. 13

Exhibited:
Honolulu, January 1975
Honolulu, January 1977
Kansas City, September–November 1977

A typical example of the work produced in Kyoto during the latter half of the 18th century: the elongated neck, reptilian head and graceful movement reminiscent of the work of Izumiya Tomotada and Yamaguchi Okatomo.

N51
Deer

Lacquer on wood
Signed *Kansai* (Koma Kansai I)
Late 18th/early 19th century

The design on this two-part *manju*, of a stag
and doe, is in the Rimpa style of painting and is
lacquered in slightly raised *takamakie* of gold
and silver on a dark polished wood. ground
with pewter rims.

N52
Black Panther *(Hyo)*

Black lacquered ivory, the eyes of
gold-backed tortoiseshell
Signed *Shingetsu*
20th century

N53
Seated Racoon-dog *(Tanuki)*

Roebuck antler
Signed *MHB* (Michael Birch)
Tunbridge Wells, England, 1979

N54
Stylised Swallow
(Tsubame)

Ivory, the eyes of black horn with tiny incised pupils
Signed *Dosho* (Kagei Dosho)
Osaka, 19th century

N55
Resting Mandarin Duck
(Oshidori)

Ivory, variously stained for effect, the eyes inlaid
Signed *Mitsuhiro* (Ohara Mitsuhiro)
Osaka, 19th century

Exhibited:
Honolulu, January 1977
Kansas City, September–November 1977
Minneapolis, September–October 1979

N56
Dove *(Hato)* on a roof tile

Ivory
Signed *Mitsuhiro* (Ohara Mitsuhiro)
Osaka, 19th century

Provenance:
Ann and Hy Meselson collection

Published:
Chappell and Welch, Netsuke, *The Japanese Art of Miniature Carving*, no.182

Exhibited:
Minneapolis,
April–July, 1998

N57
Bird on flowering plum branch

Ivory
Signed *Mitsuhiro* with seal (Ohara Mitsuhiro)
Osaka, 19th century

A two-part *manju* netsuke, the design delicately engraved in *katakiri* and *kebori*.

N58
Swallow *(Tsubame)* and willow branches

Walrus tusk
Signed *Mitsuhiro* with *kakihan*
(Ohara Mitsuhiro)
Osaka, 19th century

The design, like much of Mitsuhiro's work on *manju*, is engraved in *katakiri* and *kebori*.

N59
Seated Crane *(Tsuru)*

Ivory
Unsigned, style of Ohara Mitsuhiro
19th century

Provenance:
F.P. Schneider collection

Exhibited:
Los Angeles, November 1977–
February 1978

N60
Black Crow *(Karasu)* perched on a persimmon

Ivory, stained and painted, the eyes inlaid
Signed *Shigemasa*
Osaka, 19th century

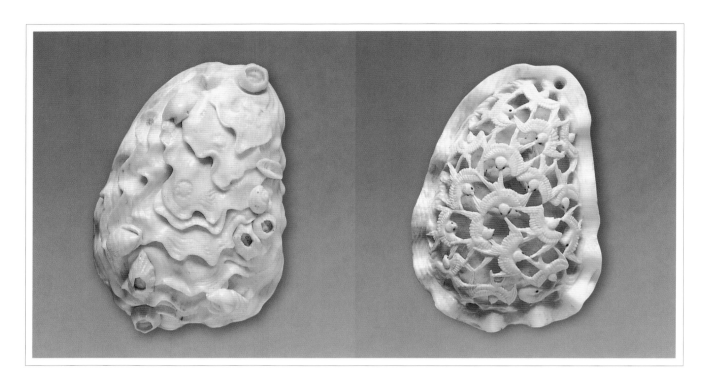

N61
Plovers *(Chidori)* in oyster shell

Ivory
Signed *Kaigyokusai* (Kaigyokusai Masatsugu)
Osaka, 19th century

Provenance:
F.P. Schneider collection

Published:
Chappell and Welch, Netsuke: *The Japanese Art of Miniature Carving*,
no. 192
Lazarnick, *NIA*, p. 563

Exhibited:
Minneapolis, April-July, 1998

The oyster shell opens on a hinge to reveal a scene of a flock of flying
plovers, carved *á jour*, while others are carved in relief below.

N62
Cuckoo *(Hototogisu)* and moon

Gold lacquer
Unsigned
19th century

A two-piece *manju*, bearing a *fundame* ground and lacquered with a large cuckoo and moon in gold *hiramakie*.

N63
Owl *(Fukuro)*

Wood and metal
Unsigned
19th century

A *kagamibuta* netsuke, the wood bowl bearing a bronze disc inlaid with an owl on a training perch, in gold, copper, *shakudo* and *shibuichi*.

N64
Swallow

Ivory and red lacquer with gold and horn inlay
Unsigned
Late 19th century

An interesting combination of materials and dates, the two parts "married" during the latter part of the 19th century. The lower half of the *manju* is of *tsuishu* (carved red lacquer) with a floral design, and was made in the 18th century, while the top is of ivory, inlaid with a small flying swallow and was produced about 100 years later.

N65
Sparrow *(Suzume)*

Boxwood with inset black eyes
Signed Yoshimichi (Kodo)
19th century

Provenance
F.P. Schneider collection

Published:
INCS, Vol. 3, no. 2 (cover)
Lazarnick, *The Signature Book*, p. 417
Lazarnick, *NIA*, vol. 2, p. 1238

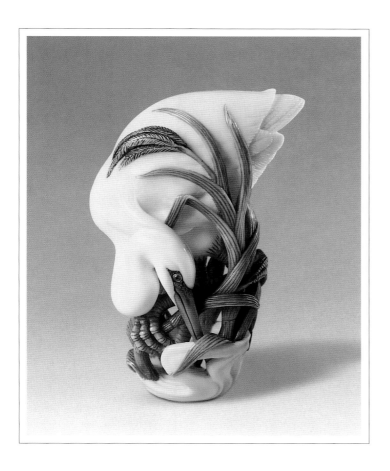

N66
Heron *(Saggi)*

Ivory, partly stained and stained with *yasha* lacquer, the eyes inlaid
Signed *Ikku* (Isamu Kasuya)
20th century

The elegant bird stands in shallows, bending to feed among reeds and grasses.

A somewhat similar example is illustrated in *Netsuke, Modern Masterpieces*, by Masayoshi Yamada, p. 24, no.5.

Published:
Chappell and Welch, Netsuke: *The Japanese Art of Miniature Carving*, no. 281

Exhibited:
Minneapolis, April–July, 1998

N67
Sparrow

Rhinoceros horn with inlaid horn eyes
Signed on a gold tablet *MHB* (Michael Birch)
Tunbridge Wells, England, c. 1975

The carving is from a peripheral section of the crown of the horn, the grain running longitudinally, creating an interesting tonal pattern.

N68
Sansukumi

Wood
Signed *Masanao*
Ise, early 19th century

Published:
Chappell and Welch, Netsuke: *The Japanese Art of Miniature Carving*, no. 190

Exhibited:
Minneapolis, April–July, 1998

The *sansukumi* is formed of the snake, frog and slug, each of which is afraid of the others. The frog would like to devour the snail and the snake would relish eating the frog. However, the poisonous secretion of the snail would be deadly to the snake and the frog.

N69
Frog *(Kaeru)* on sandal

Wood
Signed *Kokei*
Tsu, c.1800

N70
Toad on bean

Ivory and natural bean
Unsigned
19th century

The bean is almost certainly the gilla bean, known in China as *k'o tzu*, or *hsiang tou* (elephant bean), a large, flat, shiny brown vegetable, characteristically heart- or kidney- shaped and popularly used as a material for Chinese toggles.

N71
Seated Frog

Amber and mastadon tusk ivory, the eyes
inlaid
Signed with a monogram of Guy Shaw on
a gold tablet England, 2000

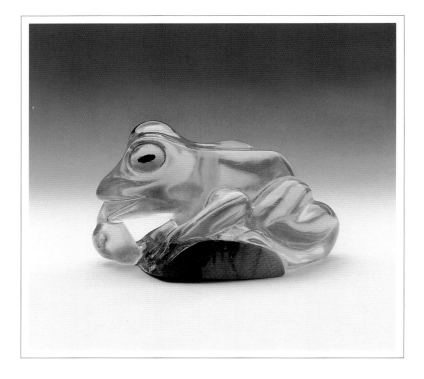

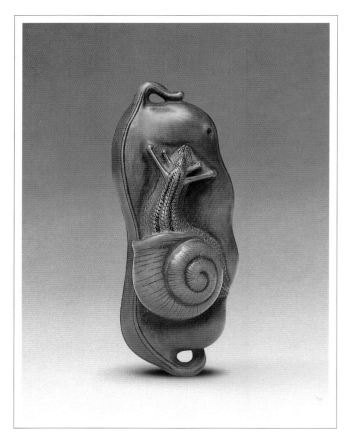

N72
Snail *(Tanishi)* on pea pod

Boxwood
Unsigned
Early 19th century

N73
Snail

Wood
Signed with *ukibori* characters, *Tadatoshi*
Nagoya, 19th century

Exhibited:
Los Angeles, November 1977–February 1978

N74
Snail on broken bucket

Wood
Signed *Masanao*
Ise, 19th century

Published:
INCS, Vol. 3, no. 2, p. 17, fig. 3

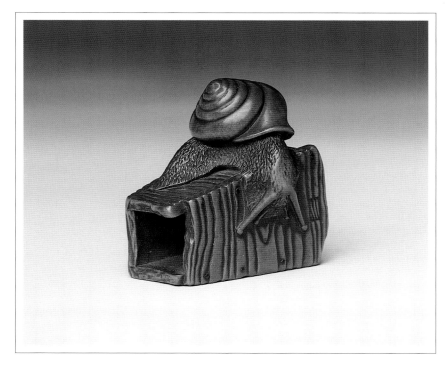

N75
Snail on bamboo section

Ivory
Signed *Mitsuhiro* with seal *Ohara*
Osaka, 19th century

Exhibited:
Honolulu, January 1977
Kansas City, September–November 1977
Minneapolis, September–October 1979

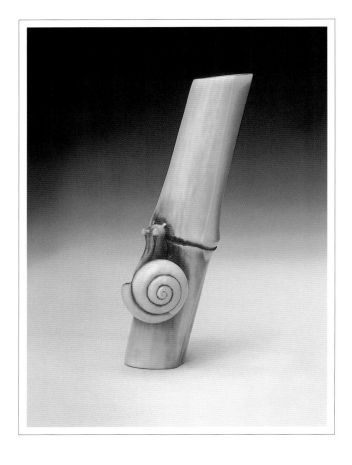

N76
Snail on fruiting branch

Ivory
Signed in a rounded rectangular reserve
Mitsuhiro (Ohara Mitsuhiro)
Osaka, 19th century

N77
Snail on two curled leaves

Boxwood
Signed *Gyokuso* (Ouchi Gyokuso)
Tokyo, late 19th/early 20th century

Exhibited:
Honolulu, January 1975
Minneapolis, September–October 1979
Honolulu, January 1983

N78
Snail on driftwood

Lacquered wood and ivory
Signed *Umaroku* (Kodo Okuda)
c.1979

Published:
Chappell and Welch, Netsuke: The Japanese Art of Miniature Carving, no. 286

Exhibited:
Minneapolis, April–July 1998

N79
Old Turtle
(Minogame)

Ivory
Unsigned
18th century

Provenance:
Anne Hull Grundy collection

It has often been recorded that the *minogame* was a mythical creature, an elderly turtle that had grown a long tail. However, it is more likely that it is a real turtle to the shell of which, over time, weed has adhered, trailing out at the back like a tail.

N80
Tortoise *(Kame)* and Young

Boxwood
Signed in an oval reserve *Tomokazu* (Kano Tomokazu)
Gifu, early 19th century

Exhibited:
Los Angeles, November 1977–February 1978

N81
Three Fish

Shagreen and lacquer
Unsigned
19th century

The large flat fish is of shagreen (probably from ray skin), its eyes of mother-of-pearl with tiny black pupils, while the two eel-like fish are lacquered in *rogin-nuri* on a *fundame* ground.

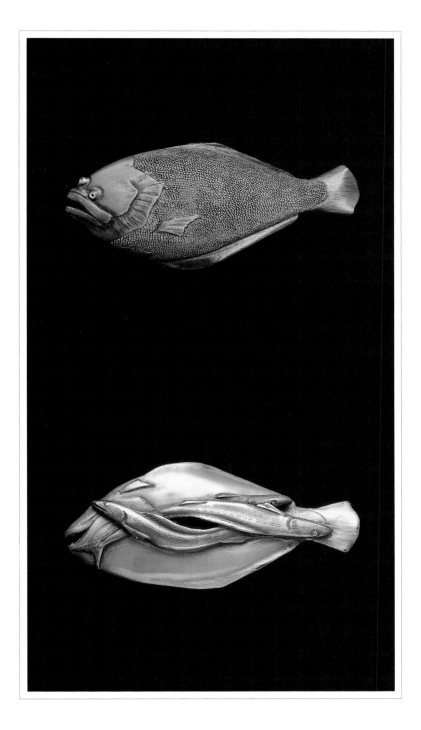

N82
Fish

Mother-of-pearl
Unsigned
19th century

Provenance
Paul Bernheimer collection

Published:
INCS, Vol. 3, no. 2, p. 19, fig. 25

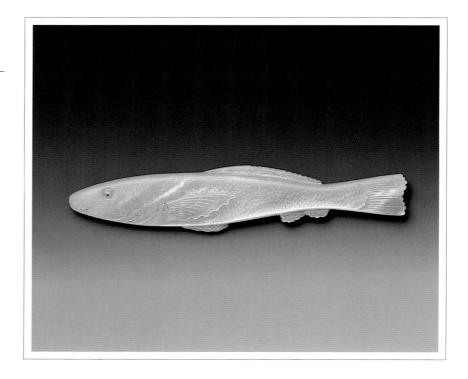

N83
Cuttlefish Bone *(Ika)*

Ivory
Signed *Jugyoku* (Ryukosai Jugyoku I)
Edo, 19th century

Provenance:
F.P. Schneider collection

N84
Cuttlefish
Bone

Ivory
Signed *Mitsuhiro*
with *kakihan* (Ohara Mitsuhiro)
Osaka, 19th century

Provenance:
Murakami collection
W.W. Winkworth collection
M.T. Hindson collection

Published:
Davey, *Netsuke*, no. 94

N85
Leaping Carp *(Koi)*

Narwhal tusk, the eyes inlaid with gold
Signed on a gold tablet *MHB* (Michael
Birch)
Tunbridge Wells, England, 1979

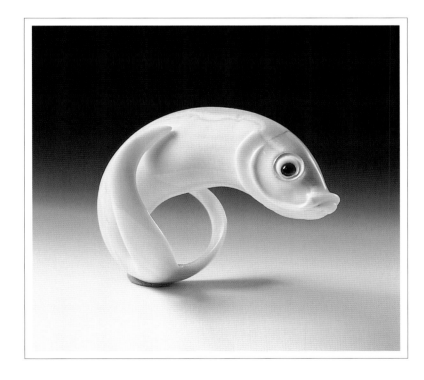

N86
Catfish (Namazu)

Walrus tusk, the eyes inlaid with gold
Signed on a silver tablet *MHB* (Michael Birch)
Tunbridge Wells, England, 1972

Published:
INCS, Vol. 4, no. 1, p. 39

N87
Catfish bound with ropes

Ivory, stained, the horn eyes with dark pupils
Signed *Ikku* (Isamu Kasuya)
Tokyo, 1986

N88
Whale *(Kujira)*

Walrus tusk
Signed *LY* (Lee Youngren)
Los Angeles, 1988

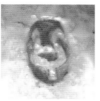

N89
Octopus *(Tako)* with aquatic leaves

Ivory, the eyes inlaid with dark horn
Unsigned
19th century

Published:
Hurtig, *Masterpieces*, no. 1

N90
Octopus on abalone
(awabi) shell

Ebony with ceramic and shell inlay
Unsigned
Mid 19th century

Published:
Chappell and Welch, Netsuke: *The Japanese Art of Miniature Carving,* no. 193

Exhibited:
Minneapolis, April–July 1998

The octopus rests on the large shell, its tentacles trailing over small waves and seaweed with inlaid silver spray drops. The *himotoshi* is formed by a large scallop shell beneath.

N91
Squid *(Ika)*

Ivory, the eyes of amber or horn with
dark pupils
Unsigned
19th century

A long, upright composition, unusually
made in two halves.

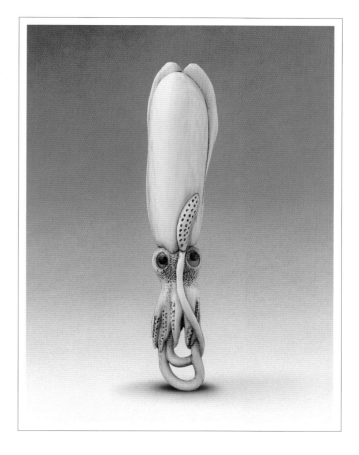

N92
Small Crab *(Kani)* on a
rolled lotus leaf

Tooth ivory, the eyes of black coral
Unsigned
19th century

N93
Small Crab on *aoi* leaves

Tortoiseshell
Unsigned
Early to mid 19th century

Provenance:
M.M. Hepworth collection
M.T. Hindson collection
Theodore Hahn collection

Published:
Davey, *Netsuke*, no. 1293

N94
Small Crab on driftwood

Stag antler, the eyes of black coral
Signed on a gold tablet *MB* (Michael Birch)
Tunbridge Wells, England, 1984

N95
Abalone *(Awabi)* Shell with small clam shells

Wood
Signed *Tomonobu*
Nagoya, 19th century

N96
Abalone *(Awabi)* Shell with vegetables

Stag antler
Signed *Hozan*
19th century

The half shell contains five aubergines *(nasubi)* one squash *(tonasu)* and a bean *(mame.)*

N97
Natural Shell

Shell, with varied inlay
Unsigned
Late 19th century

The shell is a member of the *conidae* family, with a central insert of iron and with tiny inlaid shells of gold and silver metal, among inlaid silver spray drops.

N98
Cicada *(Semi)* on twig

Umimatsu
Unsigned
Late 18th/early 19th century

The cicada and twig are made in two parts, cleverly joined together, from a dark section of *umimatsu*. The material was previously considered by collectors to be synonymous with coral. However, *umimatsu* is an organic, resinous material, while black coral is animal, being composed of numerous live polyps.

N99
Cicada on rotting leaf, a Spider beneath

Wood
Signed *Harumitsu*
Ise, 19th century

Provenance:
Raymond and Frances Bushell collection

Published:
Chappell and Welch, Netsuke: *The Japanese Art of Miniature Carving*, no. 237

Exhibited:
Minneapolis, April–July 1998

N100
Wasp
(Koshi-boso)

Bone, lacquered in
takamori style
Signed *Ikkokusai*
19th century

The large wasp is lacquered over an irregular piece of bone, perforated at one end, a loose peg forming the cord attachment.

It is difficult to ascertain which of the seven generations of lacquerers using the name Ikkokusai produced the present example. Each of them used the technique known as *takamorie*, or *Ikkokusai-nuri*, a distinctive form of high relief lacquer, built up in layers with a paste of powdered clay and lacquer, before being painted with bright colours. (see also S73)

N101
Wasp eating a
rotting pear

Wood, the eyes inlaid
Signed in a raised inlaid reserve
Kogetsu
Nagoya, 19th century

Published:
Hurtig, *Masterpieces*, no. 8
Lazarnick, *The Signature Book*, p. 236

Exhibited:
Los Angeles, Nov 1977–February 1978

The work is typical of the "Wasp in pear" carvers, whom Bushell discussed in his book *Collectors' Netsuke*, pp. 83/84. The pimples on the skin of the pear are typically carved in *ukibori,* a technique in which the pimples are impressed into the wood, the surface is shaved down to the bottom of the pimples and then the entire piece is soaked in water overnight, causing the pimples to rise above the newly created surface. The technique was used by all the "Wasp" carvers, as well as by Tametaka of Nagoya and several of the carvers from Iwami.

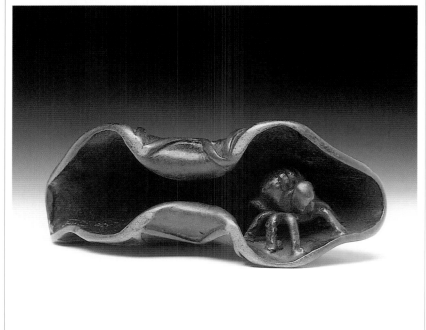

N102
Spider on lotus leaf

Sentoku
Unsigned
19th century

N103
Shishi and cub

Ivory, the eye pupils inlaid
Unsigned
Kyoto, 18th century

N104
Shishi

Ivory and *shibuichi*
Signed with the *kakihan* of Yokoya Somin III
or IV
19th century

The *shishi* is delicately engraved in *katakiri* and *kebori*, techniques favoured by the Yokoya family of metalworkers.

N105
Shishi-head with loose lower jaw

Fruitwood, the eyes of silver and *shakudo*
Signed *Sensho*
Probably early 19th century

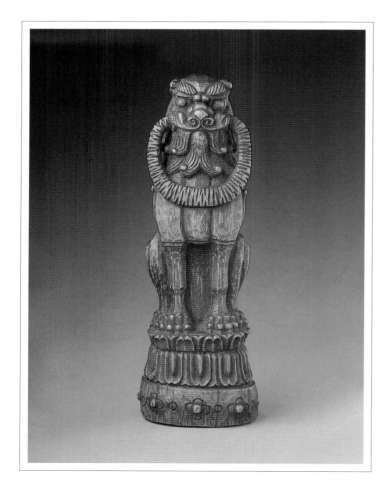

N106
Formalised seated *Shishi*

Bamboo
Signed *Toen* with seal and inscription
Nara, mid to late 19th century

Exhibited:
Honolulu, 1977

Published:
Lazarnick, *The Signature Book*, p.384
Lazarnick, *NIA*, p. 1096

The inscription reads, *Shosoin, hoko, heigoro no shishi baku, Morikawa Toen* with seal (Copy of handled incense burner of *shishi* in the Shosoin Treasure House, by Morikawa Toen).

N107
Seated *Kirin*

Walrus tusk, the eye pupils inlaid
Unsigned
18th century

N108
Suisei

Tooth ivory
Unsigned
Early 19th century

Provenance:
Dr. H.A. Gunther collection, no. 557
M.T. Hindson collection

Published:
Davey, *Netsuke*, no. 1001

The *suisei* is a comparatively rare manifestation of the *kirin*, identified by the tortoise-like carapace on its back and a single horn. The base on the present example was probably intended for a seal.

N109
Seated *Baku*

Boxwood
Unsigned
c.1800

Published:
Hurtig, *Masterpieces*, no. 5

Exhibited:
Honolulu, January 1975
Honolulu, January 1977
Kansas City, September–November 1977

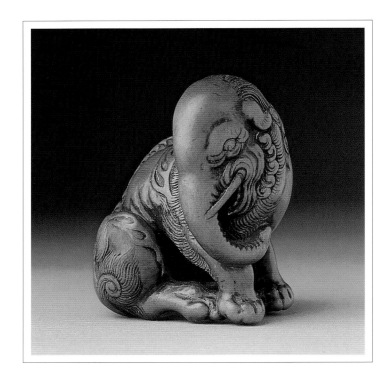

N110
Kappa on cucumber

Stag-antler, the eyes inlaid in brass with
umimatsu pupils
Unsigned
Asakusa, second half of the 19th century

The baby-faced *kappa* clings to the top of a
long cucumber. There is an obvious erotic
implication in this *sashi* style netsuke, in that
the *kappa* is a creature known to be partial to
young women and the cucumber is of phallic
appearance.

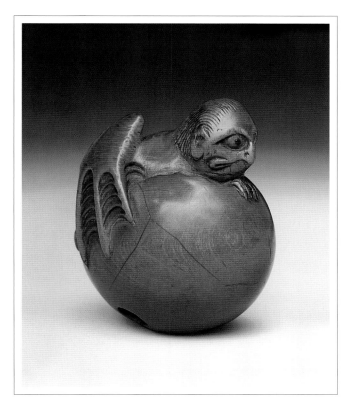

N111
Tengu hatching from egg *(Tengu no tamago)*

Boxwood
Signed *Jobun*
Edo, 18th century

Provenance:
Katchen collection

Published:
Hurtig, *Masterpieces*, no. 26

The work is typical of Jobun's rather naive style, of simple form, but with great expression.

N112
Head of Mythical Creature

Bone
Unsigned
19th century

The head appears to be of a ram and is possibly derived from a Chinese archaic bronze implement.

N113
Buddhist Disciple *(Rakan)*

Ivory (possibly mammoth tusk)
Unsigned
Late 17th/early 18th century

Published:
INCS, Vol. 3, no. 2, p. 19, fig. 22

A Chinese style *(tobori)* netsuke, somewhat worn and well patinated, giving the appearance of Chinese Ming dynasty ivory. A single engraved character, *Kore (ze),* has probably been added later to the underside.

N114
Buddhist disciple

Ivory with metal, coral and glass inlay
Signed *Suzuki Kosai*
Tokyo, 19th century

The *rakan* is shown as a bust portrait, carved in *shishiaibori* and with inlaid earrings, the reverse lightly engraved with a breaking wave.

N115
Buddhist Angel *(Tennin)*

Ivory
Unsigned
Early 19th century

A Ryusa style manju, carved and pierced with an angel flying among pierced clouds, holding a lotus bud on a stalk.

N116
Futen

Kagamibuta of ivory and *shakudo*
Unsigned
19th century

The wind god is shown making or repairing a fan and is inlaid in gold, silver and copper.

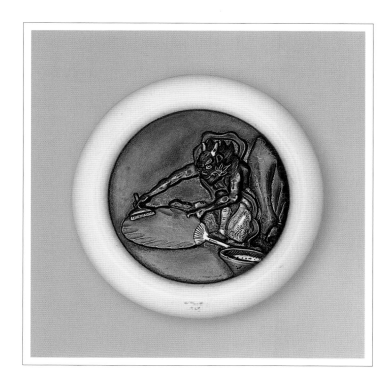

N117
Ryujin

Painted wood *(saishiki)*
Unsigned, style of Yoshimura Shuzan
Osaka, 18th century

Provenance:
Lilla Perry collection

Ryujin, known as the Dragon King of the Sea, stands holding the sacred *tama* (tide ruling jewel), a dragon at his back.

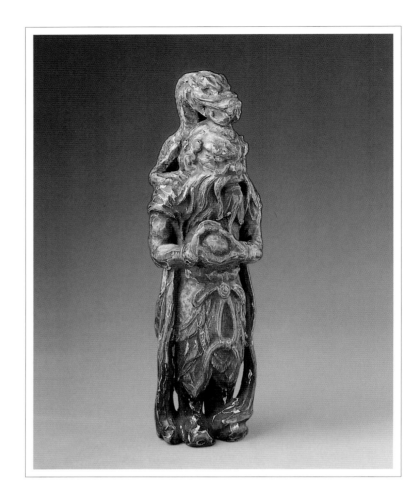

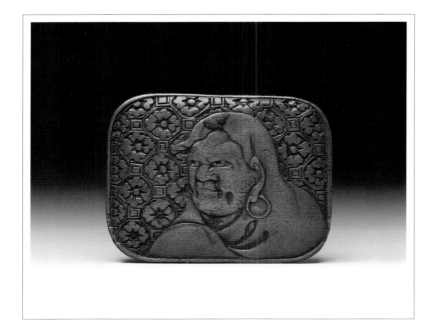

N118
Daruma

Boxwood
Unsigned
19th century

A flat oblong *manju,* the Zen patriarch carved in relief on an *asa-no-ha* ground.

N119
Toy Daruma

Wood
Signed *Sukeyuki*
Takayama, 19th century

Provenance:
F.P. Schneider collection

N120
Daruma's Fly Switch
(Hossu)

Ivory, stained
Unsigned
Late 18th/early 19th century

The *hossu* forms an elegant *sashi* netsuke and incorporates the face and hand of the Zen patriarch, the handle carved with a serpent's head.

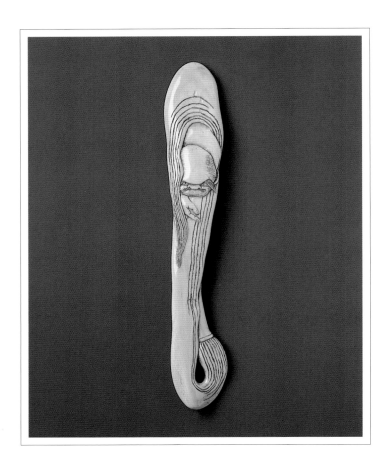

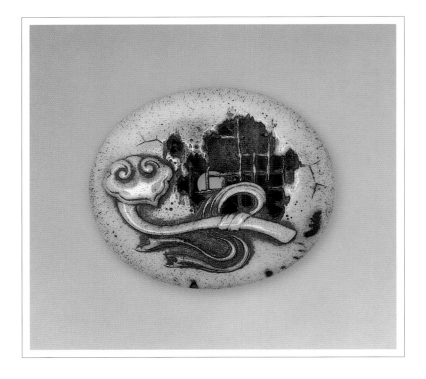

N121
Priest's Alms Bowl and Sceptre

Stag antler
Signed *Koku* (Ozaki Kokusai)
Edo, 19th century

Published:
Hurtig, Masterpieces, no. 15

A netsuke of *manju* form, carved and pierced in *ryusa* style.

N122
Temple Gong *(Mokugyo)* with Shishi

Walrus tusk
Unsigned, style of Ishikawa Rensai
Edo, 19th century

N123
Gama *Sennin*

Boxwood
Signed *Yoshikata* saku
Late 18th century

Published:
Hurtig, *Masterpieces*, no. 42
INCS, Vol. 4, no. 2, p. 22, fig. 1
Lazarnick, *The Signature Book*, p.416
Lazarnick, *NIA*, p. 1233

N124
Tobosaku *Sennin*

Ivory
Unsigned
18th century

Provenance
Roberta Pincus collection

Published:
INCS, vol.4, no. 2, p. 23, fig. 8

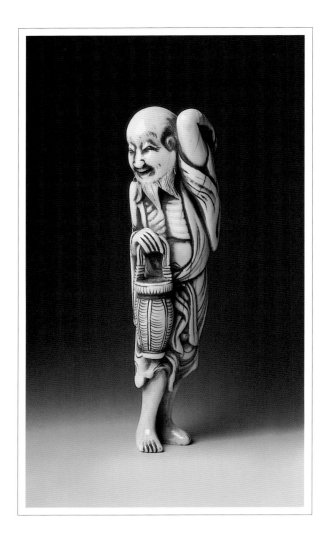

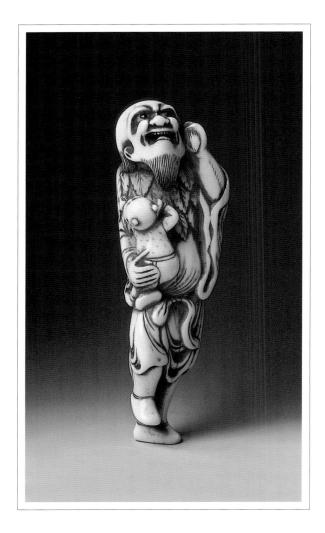

N125
Sennin with child

Ivory
Unsigned
18th century

Published:
INCS, Vol. 4, no. 2, p. 23, fig. 7

The old man is holding the child and is playfully pulling a curl of hair over his left ear, the gesture imitated by the child.

N126
Seiobo *Sennin*

Boxwood
Signed *Hokuetsu Daieido*
19th century

Provenance:
Raymond and Frances Bushell collection

Published:
Bushell, *NFU,* no. 276

The carving, of peach form, is in two parts and bears the head of Seiobo, popularly known as Queen Mother of the West, in relief. The name *Daieido* is probably a *go* (art name), while the prefix *Hokuetsu* refers to the province of Echigo from whence, it can be assumed, the artist emanated.

N127
Heavenly Processional Scene

Ivory
Signed *Kaigyokusai Masatsugu*
Osaka, 19th century

Provenance:
F. P. Schneider collection

Published:
INCS, vol. 1, no. 4, p. 12, figs. 10 and 11

Exhibited:
Honolulu, January 1975

The netsuke is in the form of a peach, opening to reveal the scene of a deity, possibly intended for Seiobo, being drawn in a carriage among clouds by six attendants.

N128
Stylised Dosojin

Rhinoceros horn and bull elephant ivory
Signed on a gold tablet *MHB* (Michael Birch)
Tunbridge Wells, England, 1977

Published:
Miriam Kinsey, *Living Masters of Netsuke*, no. 184
NK, vol. 16, no. 2, p. 42

Exhibited:
Contrasting Styles, London, 1980, no. 102

Dosojin was the god of roads and one of several gods of a primordial religion that pre-dated Shintoism. The god was often shown as two lovers, a concept that has been adopted by Michael Birch in the present example, the couple standing and locked in an embrace. The artist's interpretation incorporates the lovers, phallicism, *yin/yang*, male/female and several less obvious images.

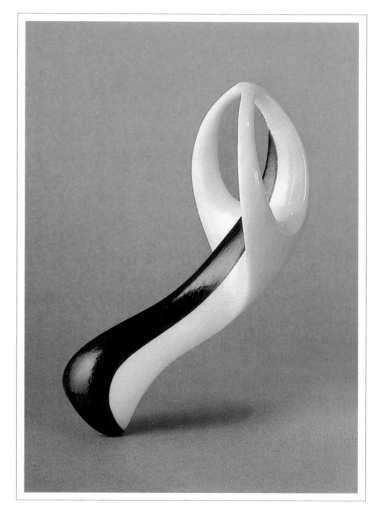

N129
Hotei

Negoro lacquered wood
Unsigned
18th century

Provenance:
Heinz and Eva Kaempfer collection

N130
Hotei holding a sack of treasure

Ivory
Unsigned
18th century

The god of contentment is shown holding the sack over his head as he fords a shallow stream.

N131
Hotei

Ivory
Signed *Mitsuhiro* with seal
Ohara on elephant
silhouette
Osaka, 19th century

The figure is a copy of a Bizen stoneware model of Hotei, of a type that was popular during the late Edo period.

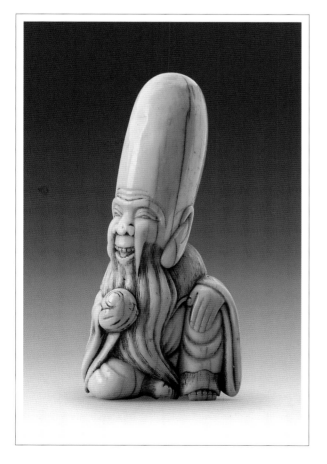

N132
Fukurokuju

Ivory
Unsigned
18th century

Provenance:
Lazarnick collection

Fukurokuju, god of longevity is often mistaken for his equally tall-headed companion Jurojin, the god of wisdom.

N133
Jurojin

Ivory
Signed *Gyokusen*
Edo, late 19th century

The god of wisdom is being gently mocked, having his tall head shaved by a small boy who climbs a ladder to accomplish his task. He is identified by the scrolls attached to his staff.

N134
Fukurokuju

Wood
Unsigned
18th century

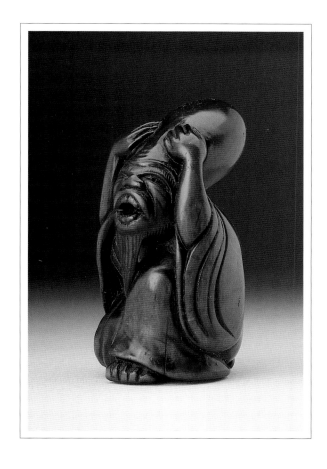

N135
Jurojin

Ivory
Signed *Norishige*
Edo, 19th century

N136
Shoki

Ivory, the eyes of horn
Signed *Jugyoku* with *kakihan*
(Ryukosai Jugyoku I)
Edo, 19th century

The demon queller is carved in deep *shishiaibori*, while the reverse shows an *oni* mask engraved in *katakiri* and *kebori*.

N137
Shoki

Ivory
Signed *Dosho* with *kakihan*
Osaka, 19th century

The demon queller is carved on the face of the rounded square *manju* netsuke, in *takabori* and *shishiaibori*, his chrysanthemum dress design engraved in *kebori*.

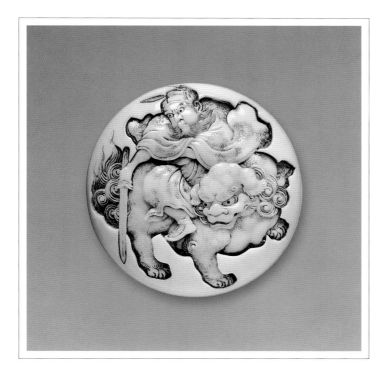

N138
Shoki riding a *shishi*

Ivory
Signed *Moritoshi* with *kakihan*
Edo-Tokyo, late 19th century

The carving, executed in the fine *shishiaibori* associated with the artist, shows Shoki on the back of a *shishi* and chasing an *oni*, the fleeing demon engraved on the reverse.

N139
Shoki and an *Oni*

Boxwood, the eye pupils inlaid
Signed *Ikkosai*
Late 18th/early 19th century

Provenance:
Katchen collection

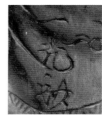

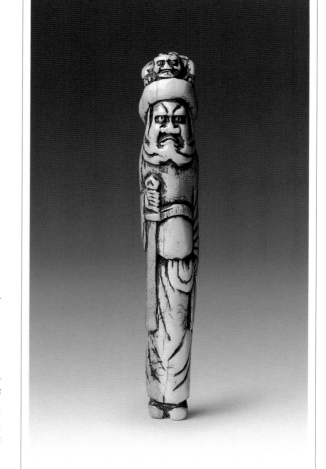

N140
Shoki and an *Oni*

Stag-antler
Unsigned
18th century

Shoki stands, bearing a stern expression, while an *oni* hides on his hat. The form is of *sashi* type, the elongated figure of the demon queller carved with great expression and the *himotoshi* passing through the two sleeves of his robe.

N141
Shoki and an *Oni*

Kagamibuta of ivory and *shibuichi*
Signed *Ryumin* with *kakihan*
19th century

The demon queller stands, while a reformed oni, holding a rosary, stands behind him.

N142
Shoki and an *Oni*

Kagamibuta of ivory and silver
Signed *Shojosai Tenmin*
19th century

The design is delicately engraved in *katakiri* and *kebori*.

N143
Oni and Gaki

Wood, the eyes of horn and ivory
Unsigned
Late 18th century

Provenance:
W.L. Behrens collection, no. 3276, illus.
Pl. XXXIX
Dr. H.A. Gunther collection
W.W. Winkworth collection
F. Meinertzhagen collection
M.T. Hindson collection

Published:
The Meinertzhagen Card Index in the
British Museum
Davey, *Netsuke,* no.1182
Hurtig, *Masterpieces,* no. 17
Chappell and Welch, Netsuke: *The
Japanese Art of Miniature Carving,*
no. 51

Exhibited:
Minneapolis, April–July 1998

The *oni* is being massaged by a *gaki*
(a tormented spirit), probably that of
a blind masseur.

N144
Ashinaga and Tenaga

Stained boxwood
Unsigned
Late 18th century

Provenance
F.P. Schneider collection

Published:
Hurtig, *Masterpieces*, no. 23

Exhibited:
Honolulu, January 1975

The legendary long-armed fisherman seated on his long-legged companion's back and reaching down to grasp an octopus.

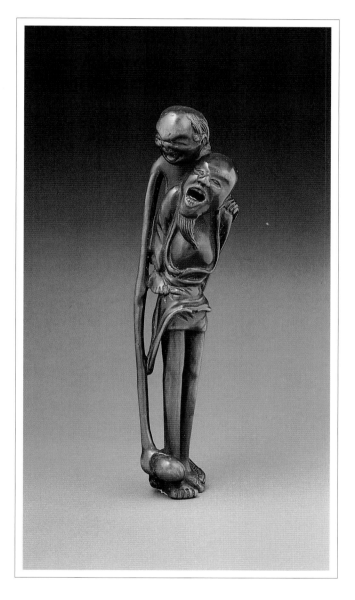

N145
Kiyohime and the Bell of Dojoji

Ebony
Signed *Minko* (Tanaka Minko) with inscription
Dated 1789

Provenance:
C.H.W. Mander collection
F. Meinertzhagen collection
W.W. Winkworth collection
M.T. Hindson collection

Published:
Davey, *Netsuke*, no. 644
MCI, p. 510
Chappell and Welch, Netsuke:
The Japanese Art of Miniature Carving,
no. 61

Exhibited:
Minneapolis, April–July 1998

The inscription beneath reads *Toki ni Tsuchino to tori chu ka isu han sanjin Minko cho with kakihan.* (Carved by Minko, a retired Daimyo of Tsu, during the middle Summer of the 46th cyclical year) (beginning 1744), i.e. 1789).

N146
Kiyohime and the Bell of Dojoji

Ivory
Unsigned
18th century

Published:
Chappell and Welch: *Netsuke, The Japanese Art of Miniature Carving*, no. 29

Exhibited:
Minneapolis, April–July 1998

The girl/witch is shown, as usual, wound around the bell of Dojoji, in which she entrapped the priest Anchin. Unusually, the stomach of the girl forms a subtle but unmistakable phallus, a fine example of lateral Japanese erotic humour.

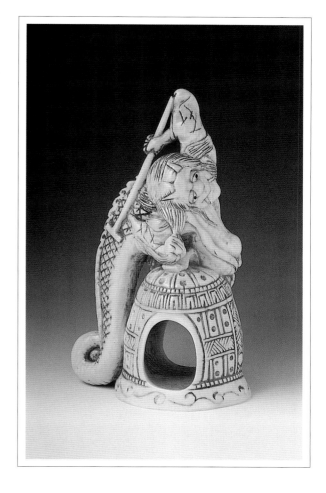

N147
Kiyohime and the Bell of Dojoji

Bronze ash tray netsuke
Unsigned
18th century

Published:
INCS, Vol. 3, no. 2, p. 19, fig. 28

N148
Okame

Plumwood
Unsigned
19th century

Provenance
Katchen collection

Published:
Hurtig, *Masterpieces,* no. 11

She holds her stomach with both hands, and with a pained expression. An inscription on the soles of both feet reads, *Kune yama, Shun sui* (sunset [on the] mountain, spring water).

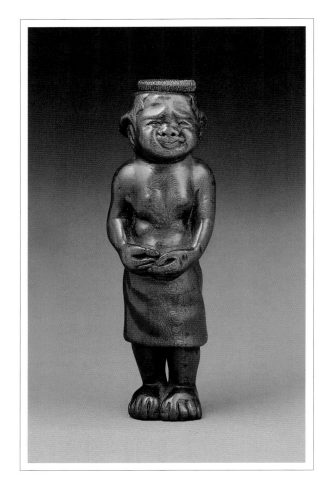

N149
Okame

Ivory, with tortoiseshell detail
Signed in a reserve with stippled surround *Mitsuhiro* (Ohara Mitsuhiro) Osaka, 19th century

Provenance:
Harry Seymour Trower collection, no. 778

Published:
The Seymour Trower collection, pl. VIII
H.L. Joly, *Legends,* facing p. 382 (original edition)
Chappell and Welch, Netsuke, *The Japanese Art of Miniature Carving,* no. 153

Exhibited:
Minneapolis, April–July 1998, no. 153

N150
Seated Okame

Ivory
Signed *Tomomitsu*
Edo, late 19th century

Provenance:
F.P. Schneider collection

N151
Okame and an *Oni*

Wood
Signed *Minko* with
kakihan (Tanaka Minko)
Tsu, late 18th century

Provenance:
W.L. Behrens collection, no. 4498, illus. pl. LVII
W. Guest collection
P. Corbin collection
M.T. Hindson collection

Published:
Neil K Davey, *Netsuke,* no. 645
Hurtig, *Masterpieces,* no. 28

Okame sits in a small round tub, having her back washed by an *oni* who stands at the side. The *kakihan* clearly shows the evolution from the character *Min*.

N152
Oni and Okame Masks

Stag antler with metal inlay
Signed *Koku* (Ozaki Kokusai)
Edo, 19th century

A *manju* netsuke, formed from the foot of an antler, with fitted insert of a large copper *oni* head with gold eyes and fangs, a small silver Okame mask inlaid on the reverse.

N153
Okame and *Oni* Masks

Ivory
Signed *Kosai* (Kosai Moritoshi)
Edo, 19th century

Provenance:
Melvin and Toyoko McGovern collection

A *manju* netsuke of *mokko* form, carved in low relief with the masks of Okame and an *oni,* the cords of the former trailing over the edge.

N154
Enshi

Wood, with ivory
inlay
Signed, on an inlaid
aogai tablet, *Ryukei*
Edo, early to mid 19th century

Provenance:
T. Brown Belfield collection, University of
Pennsylvania

Published:
Chappell and Welch, Netsuke: *The Japanese
Art of Miniature Carving,* no. 99

Exhibited:
Minneapolis, April–July 1998

Enshi (Ch: Yen Tsze) was one of the
twenty-four paragons of filial piety. As a
boy, he disguised himself in the skin of a
stag and went to the mountains to get
milk from a doe, this being the only
remedy for the eye disease suffered by his
mother. For this, he was initially chastised
by a party of hunters, until they heard his
story.

N155
Yoko

Ivory
Unsigned
Early 19th century

Yoko (Ch: Yang Hiang), another of the paragons of filial piety, was a boy who, when he was fourteen, accompanied his father to the mountains where a large tiger attacked them. He leapt in front of his father, saving him, but in doing so was killed by the great beast.

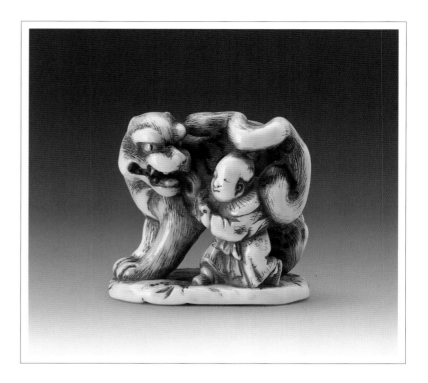

N156
Gomo

Ivory
Unsigned
Late 18th/early 19th century

Gomo (Ch: Wu Meng) was another of the twenty-four paragons of filial piety. As a young boy, he allowed mosquitoes to bite him without brushing them off his skin, while sleeping in the same room as his parents to ensure that they were not bitten or otherwise disturbed. In later life, he became a renowned magician.

N157
Ono no Komachi

Wood
Signed *Minkoku* (Genryosai Minkoku I)
Edo, Late 18th century

Published:
Chappell and Welch, Netsuke: *The Japanese Art of Miniature Carving,* no. 64

Exhibited:
Minneapolis, April–July, 1998

Ono no Komachi was a beautiful poetess of the 9th century, whose works became renowned before she fell into an impoverished old age, reduced to begging, following an unrequited love affair.

N158
Reclining Woman with child

Ivory
Unsigned
Late 17th/early 18th century

The woman is probably intended for Yama Uba, the generic name for a woman/spirit, one of whom was the mother of Kintaro, the legendary strong boy of Japan and the subject of a *No* play.

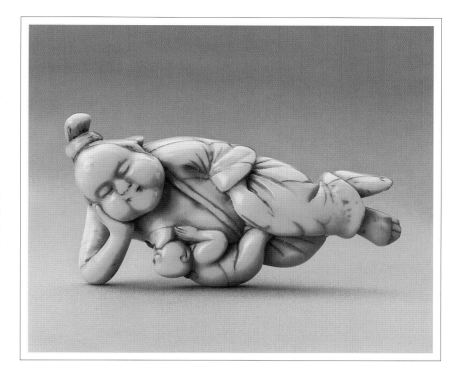

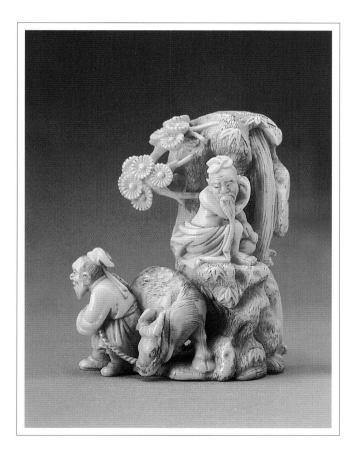

N159
Kyoyu and Sofu

Ivory
Unsigned
18th century

Published:
Chappell and Welch, *Netsuke: The Japanese Art of Miniature Carving,* no. 100

Exhibited:
Minneapolis, April–July 1998

Kyoyu (Ch: Hsiu Yu) and Sofu (Ch'ao Fu), legendary Chinese sages, were paragons of virtue. They are generally shown as here: Kyoyu washing his ears in a waterfall, to banish the temptation to which he had been subjected, while Sofu leads his ox in a stream.

N160
Ota Dokan

Ivory
Signed *Yoshitomo*
19th century

Provenance:
Michael Hauter collection

The story of Ota Dokan is based on a well-known pun. The hero, caught in a sudden heavy rainstorm, stopped at a farmhouse and asked a country girl for a raincoat *(mino)*. She withdrew briefly and returned, proffering him a spray of yellow roses *(yamabuki)* on a fan. Infuriated, Ota Dokan rushed away and only later did he remember the well-known poem and marvelled at the girl's knowledge and subtleness. The poem is of Japanese love and translates, "Though the yamabuki has many petals, I grieve that it has no seed *(mino)*," implying she had no raincoat to spare.

N161
Kan'u

Ivory
Signed *Naohiro*
Edo, 19th century

The Chinese general is carved in *shishiaibori,* shown in typical attitude, stroking his beard.

N162
Chohi

Ivory
Signed in an oval reserve *Ikko*
Early 19th century

Published:
Hurtig, *Masterpieces,* no. 4

Chohi (Ch: Chang Fei) was one of the three famous Chinese generals of the Han dynasty, together with Kan'u (Guanti) and Gentoku (Liu Pi).

N163
Ii no Hayata slaying the *Nue*

Ivory
Unsigned
Early 19th century

Provenance:
W. L. Behrens collection, no. 1163
Guest collection, no. 1638
V.F. Weber collection, no. 210
M.T. Hindson collection

Published:
V.F. Weber, *Koji Hoten,* pl. LXX
Davey, *Netsuke,* no. 1051
Chappell and Welch, Netsuke: *The Japanese Art of Miniature Carving,* no. 107

Exhibited:
Minneapolis, April–July 1998

Ii no Hayata was the retainer of Minamoto no Yorimasa who, in 1153, killed the strange beast known as the *nue,* which had been seen stalking the palace at night. Yorimasa brought it down with an arrow before Ii no Hayata dispatched it with his sword.

N164
Nitta no Shiro Tadatsune

Ivory
Unsigned
Late 18th century

Published:
Chappell and Welch, *Netsuke: The Japanese Art of Miniature Carving*, no. 108

Exhibited:
Minneapolis, April–July 1998

The hero is shown riding backwards on a running boar, which was threatening the *shogun* Minamoto no Yoritomo during a hunting expedition on the slopes of Mount Fuji in 1193. Tadatsune slew the beast and was rewarded with a large estate by Yoritomo.

N165
Minamoto no Mitsunaka

Ivory with tortoiseshell inlay
Signed *Moritoshi* with *kakihan*
(Kosai Moritoshi)
Edo, 19th century

Provenance:
H. Seymour Trower collection, no. 372
T.S. Davy collection
M.T. Hindson collection
Dr. J. and E. Kurstin collection

Published:
Davey, *Netsuke,* no. 413
Okada and Neill, *Real and Imaginary Beings,* no. 77

Several legends of heroes slaying dragons have been passed down through history, but the present example probably depicts Minamoto no Mitsunaka, described in literature as standing with one foot on the head of a dragon before dispatching it.

N166
Raiden

Ivory with *raden* inlay
Signed *Hakuyosai Shoraku*
Edo, 19th century

Provenance:
Michael Tomkinson collection
J.A. Fairley collection
M.T. Hindson collection

Published:
Chappell and Welch, *Netsuke, The Japanese Art of Miniature Carving*, no. 158 (wrongly described as by Hakuunsai)
Davey, *Netsuke,* no. 415
MCI, p. 753

Exhibited:
Minneapolis, April–July 1998

The god of thunder is seen trapped in a spider's web, the large insect carved in relief on the reverse.

N167
Benkei

Ivory and *shibuichi*
Unsigned
19th century

A *kagamibuta,* the ivory bowl bearing a *shibuichi* disc, showing the legendary hero Benkei struck by Yoshitsune's fan during their epic dual on the Gojo bridge, inlaid in gold, copper and *shakudo.*

N168
Ronin

Boxwood
Signed *Minko juntoku* (Minko the virtuous)
Tsu, late 18th century

Published:
Chappell and Welch, *Netsuke: The Japanese Art of Miniature Carving,* no. 66
Hurtig, *Masterpieces,* no. 37
Lazarnick, *NIA,* p. 759

Exhibited:
Minneapolis, April–July, 1998

The subject has been variously described as a *ronin* (masterless *samurai*) or as Kidomaru (Hakamadare Yasusuke), the 11th century brigand who was infamous for attempting to slaughter his brother, Fujiwara Hirai Yasumasa. However, because the majority of depictions of the latter show him wearing formal dress, we feel it is more likely that the present depiction is of a *ronin*.

N169
Two *Samurai*

Ivory
Signed *Moritoshi* (Kosai Moritoshi)
Edo, 19th century

An unusual example of slapstick humour, carved in deep *shishiaibori* with two *samurai*, each hiding on opposite sides of a large tree and suddenly discovering each other. In their confusion each runs away from the other, one falling as he flees.

N170
Helmet *(Kabuto)*

Bronze
Unsigned
18th century

N171
Helmet

Metal and stag antler
Unsigned
19th century

The crown *(hachi)* is of shakudo with heavy silver studs, while the aperture *(hachimanzo)* is ringed with gold. The peak *(maezashi)* is of stag antler and is decorated with a pair of antlers and a silver arrow. The meticulously detailed neck guard *(shikoro)* is also of stag antler, as is the flowering plum carved beneath.

The helmet is that of Kajiwara Genda Kagesue, who was in the service of Minamoto no Yoritomo. He played a great part in the wars between the Taira and Minamoto clans and is best known for his race across the Uji river against Saemon no jo Sasaki Shiro Takatsuna. He was often identified in battle by the sprig of plum blossom that he carried in his quiver.

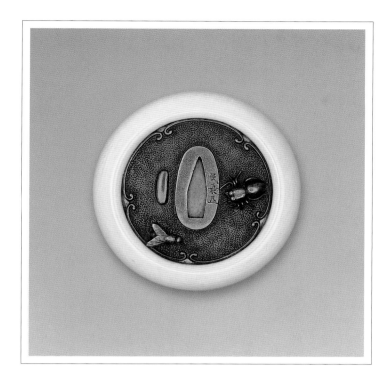

N172
Sword Guard *(Tsuba)*

Ivory and *shibuichi*
Signed *Minjo* with *kakihan*
19th century

The *shibuichi* disc is in the form of a sword guard inlaid with a fly and beetle in *shakudo takazogan*.

N173
Diving girl *(Ama)*

Ivory
Unsigned
18th century

N174
Diving Girl and Octopus

Walrus tusk
Unsigned
19th century

Provenance:
W.L. Behrens collection, no. 3881

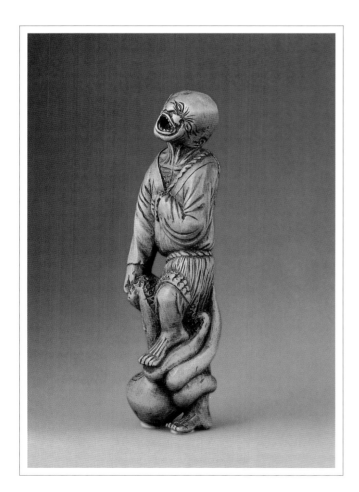

N175
Agonised Fisherman and Octopus

Boxwood
Unsigned
Early 19th century

A somewhat crudely carved and finished netsuke, akin to folk art, but highly expressive.

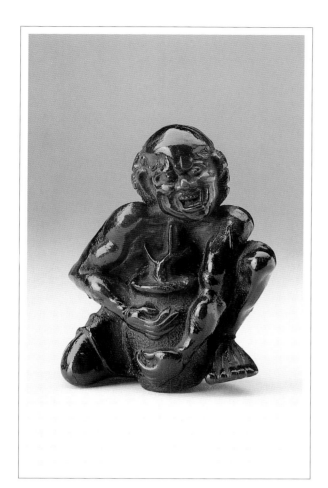

N176
Islander

Pressed horn
Unsigned
Meiji period (1868–1912)

The material is unusually clear, having an appearance not unlike amber or tortoiseshell.

N177
Tokaido Road Porter
(Kumosuke)

Wood
Unsigned
Late 18th century

Published:
INCS, Vol. 3, no. 2, p.20, fig. 39

This well-known subject, which has often been described before as a wrestler, depicts a porter at one of the fifty-three posting stations on the Tokaido Road which ran between Edo and Kyoto during the Edo period.

N178
Street Peddler

Ivory
Inscribed in an oval reserve *Tomotada*
Late 18th century

The peddler is selling rat poison, identified by the rodent seated on the box that is slung by a cord around the peddler's neck.

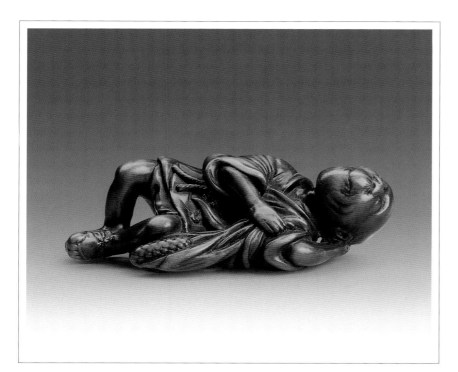

N179
Drunken Rice Farmer

Wood
Unsigned
19th century

Provenance:
Dr. J and E. Kurstin collection

Published:
Okada and Neill, *Real and Imaginary Beings*, no. 84

N180
Blind *sake* Seller

Cherrywood
Signed *Miwa*
Edo, 18th century

Published:
S.L. Moss, *Japanese Netsuke: Serious Art*, no. 20

N181
Blind Masseur
(*Amma*) and Client

Wood
Signed *Minko Tsuhan* (Daimyo of
Tsu) with *kakihan* (Tanaka Minko)
Tsu, late 18th century

Published:
Hurtig, *Masterpieces,* no. 52
Lazarnick, *NIA,* p. 763

N182
Blind Man

Ivory
Signed in an oval reserve *Komin*
Edo, mid 19th century

Provenance:
F. P. Schneider collection

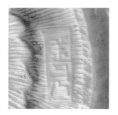

N183
Mill Stone Cutter

Ivory
Signed with *tensho* characters in a
rectangular reserve *Yoshihisa*
Edo, Meiji period (1868–1912)

Provenance:
F.P. Schneider collection

Published:
INCS, Vol. 3, no. 2, p. 20, fig 36

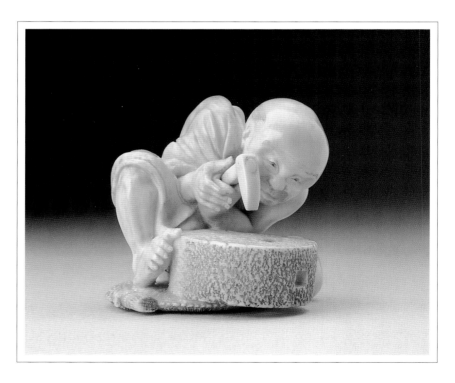

N184
Lion Dancer *(Shishimai)*

Boxwood, the mask eyes of glass
Signed *Miwa* with *kakihan*
Edo, late 18th century

N185
Player with ball on foot

Negoro lacquer over wood
Unsigned
18th century

Published:
Chappell and Welch, *Netsuke: The Japanese Art of Miniature Carving,* no. 65
Hurtig, *Masterpieces,* no. 38
INCS, Vol. 3, no. 2, p. 20. fig. 37

Exhibited:
Minneapolis, April–July 1998

The man is playing *kemari,* or Japanese football, which was introduced to Japan from China in the 7th century when it was, for the most part, played by males of the royal family and their courtiers.

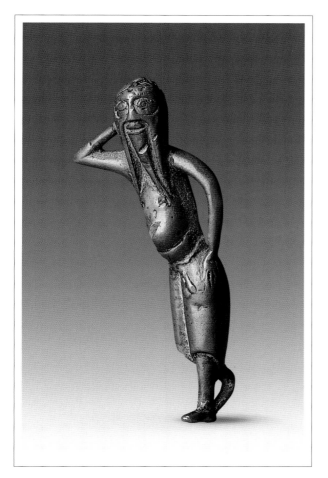

N186
Dancing Man

Bronze
Unsigned
18th century

N187
Acrobat

Boxwood
Unsigned
Edo, mid 19th century

Published:
INCS, Vol. 3, no. 2, p. 20, fig. 35

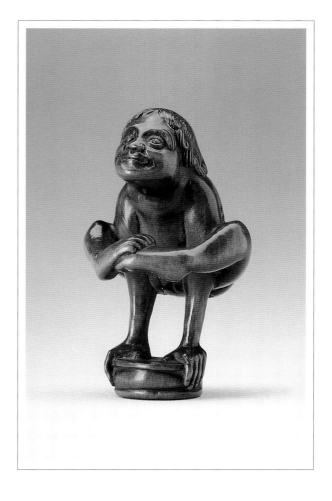

N188
Dancing Man and plum blossoms

Ivory and *shibuichi* with metal inlay
Unsigned
19th century

A *kagamibuta,* the ivory bowl bearing a *shibuichi* disc, inlaid in gold, silver, copper and *shakudo* with a man dancing, seen in silhouette behind a window, with plum blossoms outside.

N189
Courtesan *(Oiran)* with her Attendant *(Kamuro)*

Ivory
Unsigned
Probably Osaka, early 19th century

Provenance:
Dr. J. and E. Kurstin collection
Phil Bradford collection

Published:
Okada and Neill, *Real and Imaginary Beings,* no. 83
S.L. Moss, *Zodiac Beasts and Distant Cousins,* no. 72

The subject of the netsuke has been cause for debate in recent years. It has been suggested that it depicts a Kabuki actor with a diminutive *oiran*. It is in fact an *oiran* (identified by her *obi* tied at the front) with her young *kamuro*. The design appears to have been taken directly from a painting by Kaigetsudo Anchi (active 1704–1716), now in the Tokyo National Museum collection.

N190
Kabuki Play

Sperm whale tooth
Signed *Isshinsai Masayuki with kakihan*
Possibly Osaka, 19th century

The engraving depicts a scene from Act V, the *sushi* shop, from the Kabuki play, *Yoshitsune Sembonzakura.* Here is shown Gonta, the son of Yasaemon, carrying a tub containing the severed head of his retainer Kokingo.

Published:
Lazarnick, NIA, p. 747

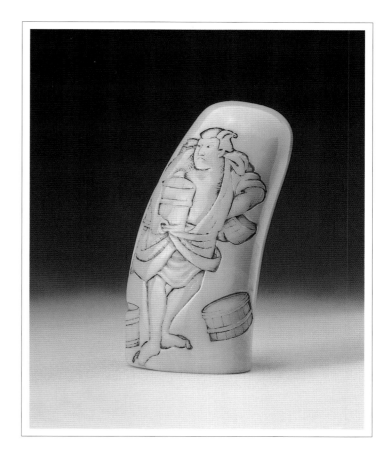

N191
Kabuki Actor

Kagamibuta of ivory and *shibuichi*
Unsigned
19th century

The actor portrayed is one of the Danjuro family, in the play *Shibaraku.* The portrait is shown in relief with details of gold and *shakudo.*

N192
Sambaso Accoutrements

Ivory
Signed *Kagetoshi*
Kyoto, 19th century

An unusual *hako* netsuke in the form of a small casket carved with pine trees and cranes, the top carved in relief with an Okina mask. The interior contains a removable scene of the audience for a performance of the Sambaso dance among *kadomatsu* (young pines).

N193
Mask of Shojo

Bizen stoneware
Stamped signature, *Sekisen*
Late 19th century

N194
Mask of Old Man

Wood
Signed *Tomin*
Early 19th century

N195
Mask of Okame

Ivory
Signed *Ryumin* with seal
19th century

N196
Mask of Shojo

Hornbill *(Hoden)*
Unsigned
19th century

Provenance:
Anne Hull Grundy collection

N197
Mask of Okina

Wood with ivory details
Signed *Masatomo*
Early 19th century

N198
Gigaku Mask of Baramon (Brahmin)

Wood, coated with lacquer and *gofun*
Signed *Tekkan* with *kakihan*
Late 19th century

The Gigaku were the oldest theatrical masks of Japan, with faces derived from China, India, Indonesia, Tibet and Iran. Baramon (the Indian Brahmin) represents the highest caste in the Indian social structure.

N199
Five Masks

Wood
Unsigned
Mid 19th century

The cluster comprising the masks of Kijo, Magojiro, Fukai, Uzume and Kintaro with his axe.

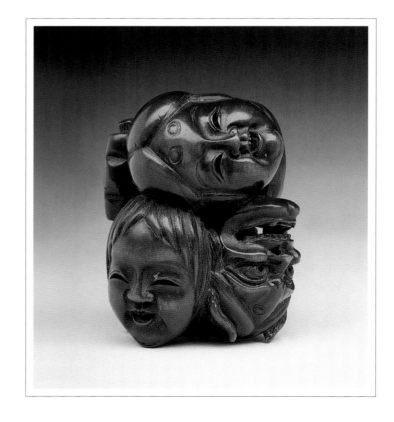

N200
Comedy and Tragedy, a Pair of Masks

Black walnut
Signed with the monogram of Anthony Towne
Eugene, Oregon, 1990

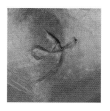

N201
Wrestlers

Ivory
Signed *Dosho saku*
Osaka, 19th century

The carving is executed in *shishiaibori* and shows one combatant grabbing the leg of his opponent and trying to throw him to the ground.

N202
Three Children

Wood
Signed *Tametaka*
Nagoya, 18th century

The children are playing at *shishimai* (lion dancing), one wearing a typical cloaked mask, while his companions play a toy trumpet and drum.

N203
Chinese Boy *(Karako)* holding a small goat

Ivory
Unsigned
Kyoto, late 18th/early 19th century

Published:
Chappell and Welch, *Netsuke, The Japanese Art of Miniature Carving*, no. 72

Exhibited:
Minneapolis, April–July 1998

N204
Herdsboy with Ox (Ushidoji)

Ivory, the eye pupils inlaid
Inscribed in a rectangular reserve *Tomotada*
Kyoto, 18th century

Provenance:
F.P. Schneider collection

N205
Three Children playing in Nara

Wood
Signed *Tadashige*
Edo, 19th century

The children are playing around the great pillar at the Daibutsu temple in Nara, a popular venue for pilgrims and for tourists. One child crawls through the large hole carved through the pillar while the others look on with delight.

N206
Childrens' Toys
(Omochazuke)

Ivory, with coral and metal details
Unsigned, style of Tokoku
Tokyo, late 19th century

The toys are a typical compilation of those popular during the late Edo period and include masks, a bird pull-toy, horn and gourd, clustered around a coral image of Daruma, holding a silver fly switch.

N207
Woman bathing

Boxwood and fruitwood
Unsigned
Late 18th century

Published:
Hurtig, *Masterpieces,* no.27

Carved in two separate pieces, the lady of boxwood resting in the fruitwood tub, the cord passing through a hole in her back and through a hole in the base of the tub.

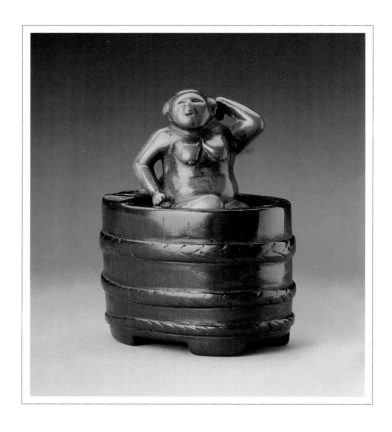

N208
Temple Guardian

Wood
Signed in a rectangular reserve *Miwa* with *kakihan*
Tsu, early 19th century

The man sits on two straw *sandals (waraji)* and grimaces with pain as he applies a burning *moxa* pellet to his leg.

N209
Woman eating

Walrus tusk
Unsigned
19th century

An unusual Ryusa-style *manju*, carved and pierced with a woman eating behind a *shoji* screen, the reverse pierced with a four-petal flower design.

N210
Ojime, carved with the Head of a Man

Ivory
Signed *Mitsuhiro* with *kakihan*
Osaka, 19th century

The head may be intended for that of Daruma

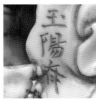

N211
Lady with an *Oni*

Ivory
Signed *Gyokuyosai*
Edo, mid to late 19th century

Published:
INCS, Vol. 3, no. 2, p. 23, fig. 33

The lady is possibly intended for Ono no Komachi in her former years as a beautiful young poetess, before she became an old beggar (see N157). She is seen here repelling the advances of a frustrated demon.

N212
Dutch Settler with cockerel

Stag antler
Unsigned
18th century

Published:
Hurtig, *Masterpieces,* no. 21

N213
Dutch Settler

Ivory, the coat buttons inlaid
Unsigned
Late 18th century

Possibly depicting a sea captain, he stands, facing ahead and holding a large telescope, his buttoned coat typically carved with breaking waves.

N214
Foreigner

Stag-antler
Unsigned
18th century

Provenance:
Jack Tropp collection

Published:
Hurtig, *Masterpieces*, no. 788

The man is probably a Dutchman, wearing a typical broad-rimmed hat and carrying a sheep.

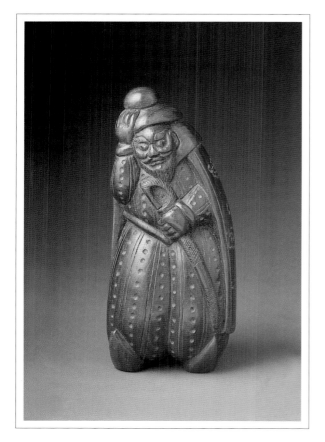

N215
Dutch Settler

Rosewood
Signed *Shosai*
20th century

He stands, wearing broad pantaloons, holding a large round hat in his right hand and clasping a sword with his left.

N216
Dutch Settler

Roebuck antler
Signed on an inlaid gold tablet
MHB (Michael Birch)
Tunbridge Wells, England, 1985

Published:
NK, Vol. 7, no. 4

N217
Matchlock Gun

Wood and metal with lacquered
details
Unsigned
19th century

N218
Matchlock
Gun

Metal
Signed *Baitetsu*
19th century

Published:
Hurtig, *Masterpieces,* no. 54

Exhibited:
Honolulu, January 1975

The gun serves both as a netsuke
and also as a *yatate* (portable brush
and ink case).

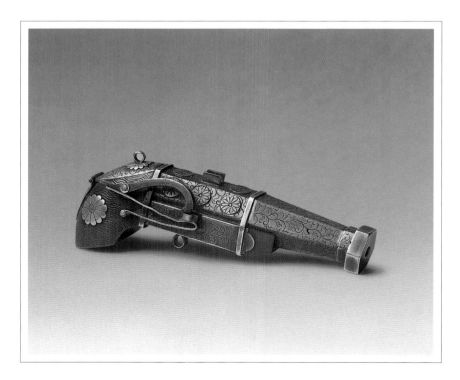

N219
Skeleton with grave post

Boxwood
Unsigned
18th century

Provenance:
Lt. Col. J.B. Gaskell collection, no. 868

Published:
INCS, Vol. 3, no. 2, p. 18, fig. 12

The human skeleton stands on a low mound base, leaning on a grave post, while holding a small grave marker, the *himotoshi* passing through the back bone.

N220
Tea Ceremony (Cha-no-yu) Utensils

Ivory
Signed *Dosho*
Osaka, 19th century

N221
Tea Ceremony Utensils

Wood with mother-of-pearl inlay
Signed *Rensha*
19th century

The utensils shown are the charcoal basket *(sumi tori)*, the feather brush for ashes *(haboki)* and a pair of iron tongs *(hibashi)*, all inlaid in mother-of-pearl on a carved diaper ground.

N222
Tea Bowl and Tea Whisk
(Chawan and Chasen)

Persimmon wood, the whisk of ivory
Signed *Yoshitomo*
Late 19th century

Provenance:
F.P. Schneider collection

Published:
INCS, Vol. 3, no. 2, p. 21, fig. 50
Hurtig, *Masterpieces,* no. 41
Lazarnick, *The Signature Book,* p. 241
Lazarnick, *NIA,* p. 1247

N223
Teakettle *(Kama)*

Wood with ivory detail
Unsigned
18th century

A simple model of a teakettle with ivory spout and handle, a ten-character poem inscribed in red lacquer to the sides.

N224
Gourd-shaped Bottle

Tsuishu lacquer with metal ring *himotoshi* and stopper
Unsigned
Late 18th century

Provenance:
F.P. Schneider collection

N225
Pipe *(Kiseru)*

Glazed pottery
Signed on bowl *Eiraku*
19th century

N226
Flint Lighter *(Hidogu)*

Shibuichi with inlays of silver and gold
Signed *Shigetsu*
19th century

A *manju*-style netsuke with a flower and butterfly design inlaid in gold and *shakudo hirazogan* and four small insects in gold and silver *takazogan*.

N227
Seals

Kagamibuta of wood and *shakudo*
Unsigned
19th century

The design is of five painters' seals, inlaid in silver on a *shakudo* ground.

N228
Silk Seal

Stag antler
Unsigned
18th century

The seal is formed from the foot of an antler with the grotesque bust of a Dutch settler on the top, a two-character seal cut beneath. This type of stamp was used in the 18th and 19th centuries on parcels of silk being traded.

N229
Fulling Block (*Kinuta*)
Tree Stump

Ivory
Signed *Mitsuhiro* with seal *Ohara*
Osaka, 19th century

Provenance:
Raymond and Frances Bushell collection

Published:
Bushell, *The Inro Handbook,* p. 30, no. 16
Lazarnick, *NIA,* vol. 1, p. 777

The roughly hewn block is engraved on the top in *katakiri* and *kebori* with a sparrow and plum blossom, the base with a fourteen character Chinese poem, *Yu yo ari kyaku tou hana kitaru, kono shi sei yuto jaku kyo:* "This clean and tranquil place is like the capital. It will be soon when people come to appreciate the flowers."

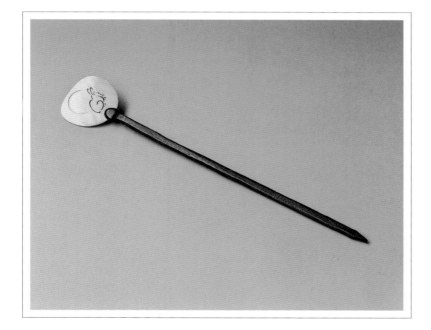

N230
Hair Ornament (*Kogai*)

Wood and ivory
Signed *Mitsuhiro* (Ohara Mitsuhiro)
Osaka, 19th century

The ivory fan-shaped top is delicately engraved with a rabbit against the full moon.

N231
Cartwheel and Vines

Stag antler and iron
Signed on an inlaid gold tablet *Ryumin*
19th century

The stag antler bowl of this *kagamibuta* bears an iron disc in the form of a cartwheel overgrown with vines in gold *takazogan*.

N232
Closed Fist

Ivory
Unsigned
Probably 18th century

The subject possibly represents a strengthening tool.

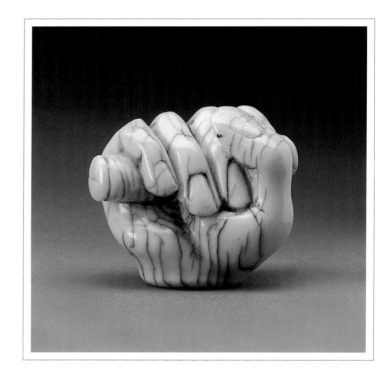

N233
Compass and Sundial
(Jishaku and Hidokei)

Brass
Unsigned
c. 1800

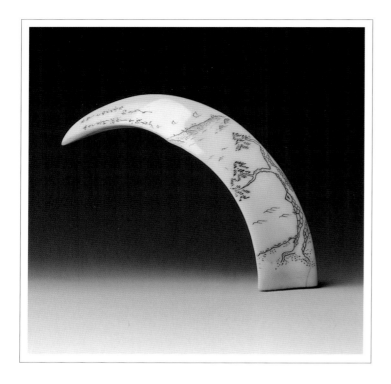

N234
Landscape and *Waka* Poem

Boar's tusk
Unsigned
Iwami, c.1800

The inscription is a *waka* (31 syllable poem) that reads, *Fuka fuka to Akashi no Urano asagiri ni Shima kakureyuki fune.... Omou.* (On the beach at Akashi in the early morning watching your boat going away through the mist).

It is assumed that this netsuke is associated with the Iwami school, although Akashi is some distance away, near Kobe.

N235
Landscape

Ebony
Signed in a sunken oval reserve *Horaku*
Kyoto, 19th century

A fine example of Horaku's landscape netsuke, carved in delicate relief in flawless wood, with around twenty-two minute figures in and around a walled pavilion with several outlying balconies on craggy rocks beneath overhanging trees.

N236
Map of Japan

Bone
Unsigned
19th century

Provenance:
M.T. Hindson collection

Published:
Davey, *Netsuke,* no. 827

The map is carefully engraved in *kebori* beneath the inscription, *Dai Nippon koku shoshin no zu* (Provinces of Japan correctly drawn). The work is in the style of Nanka and Nanyo, of Izumo, both of whom were well-known for their fine engraving in this style (see IN86).

N237
Chrysanthemum
(Kiku)

Ivory
Signed *Dosho*
Osaka, 19th century

N238
Peony *(Botan)* and Flowerball *(Kusadama)*

Kiri-wood with gold inlay
Signed in seal form *Bunsai*
19th century

Provenance:
F.P. Schneider collection

Published:
Hurtig, *Masterpieces,* no. 43

The naturalistic peonies are inlaid in gold *takazogan* while the flowerball is lacquered in *takamakie.*

N239
Lotus Leaf *(Hasa no hana)* with frog

Umimatsu with ivory, coral, silver and mother-of-pearl
Unsigned
Early 19th century

Published:
Hurtig, *Masterpieces,* p. 29, no. 34

N240
Lotus Plant with intertwined leaves, blossoms and buds

Section of stag antler
Unsigned
19th century

A *sashi* style netsuke of somewhat phallic form.

N241
Vegetables

Wood, dark stained
Unsigned
Early 19th century

An elaborate group of eight aubergines *(nasubi)* and two pumpkins *(tonasu)*, forming a compact, openwork composition.

N242
Gourd *(Hyotan)*

Guribori lacquer with metal ring *himotoshi*
and stopper
Unsigned
Probably late 18th century

N243
Gourd

Lacquered wood
Unsigned
19th century

The gourd is finely lacquered with a leaf and
tendril in *takamakie* and *e-nashiji*.

N244
Two Gourds

Ivory
Signed *Hakuryu*
Kyoto, 19th century

The larger gourd is shaped as a bird and as a hollowed out *sake* cup, edged with black lines. The smaller gourd is of slender form and attached to form the *himotoshi*. Similar examples by Mitsuhiro of Osaka have been recorded (see Bushell, *Collectors' Netsuke*, p. 99, no. 133).

N245
Gourd

Ivory
Signed *Mitsusada* with seal (Ohara Mitsusada)
Osaka, 19th century

The fruit is delicately engraved in *katakiri* and *kebori* with *oni nembutsu,* the demon carrying a drum and beater, together with a notebook, engraved with the legend *Hogacho,* intimating that it is a notebook for recording the names of donors to shrines or temples.

N246
Vines

Iron with gold inlay
Unsigned
19th century

A one piece *manju* inlaid in *hirazogan* with an over-all design of trailing vines centred on three *kiri* leaves and with pine needles on the reverse, the cord hole ringed with gold.

N247
Gourd Vine

Lacquer on red sandalwood *(shitan)*
Signed *Kanshosai*
19th century

The design is shown in gold *takamakie* and *hiramakie* on a clear lacquered wood ground, the cord hole ringed with metal on the reverse.

N248
Aubergine
(Nasubi)

Ivory
Signed Mitsuhiro
(Ohara Mitsuhiro)
Osaka, 19th century

Provenance:
Tom Evans, New Hampshire

A wonderful example of Mitsuhiro's still life groups. The large aubergine has two smaller plants attached to one side, the beautifully modulated carving enhanced by extremely fine stippling and staining. To one side is a poem in delicate *kana* script, reading, "Fascinating; even though there is a wisteria vine, a lady's wishes are still fanciful."; signed Yoshishige Suetame.

N249
Aubergine

Hirado porcelain
Unsigned
Mid19th century

Published:
INCS, Vol. 3, no. 2, p. 19, fig. 20

Exhibited:
Honolulu, 1975

The fruit is covered with a fine white glaze, two blue glazed leaves attached to the grey biscuit calyx.

N250
Tuber with Dried Fish, Chestnut and small Nuts

Ivory
Faintly signed *Mitsuhiro* with seal *Ohara*
Osaka, 19th century

The subject represents the ingredients for part of a meal, the sardine, chestnut and nuts carved in relief on the side of the tuber. The work is typical of Mitsuhiro's simplistic still life creations, enhanced by a very faint but impeccable signature.

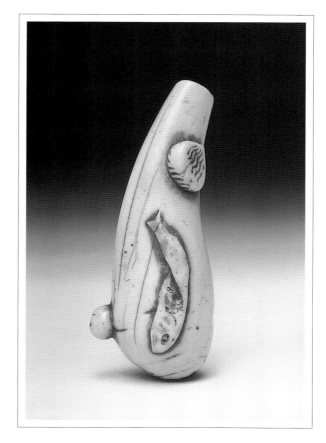

N251
Cluster of *Shiitake* Mushrooms

Ivory
Signed *Raku*
Osaka, late 18th/early 19th century

Published:
Lazarnick, NIA, p. 858

Exhibited:
Honolulu, January 1975

The single character signature has been seen on a small number of netsuke and may be intended for Risuke Garaku of Osaka.

N252
Cluster of five Mushrooms

Wood
Unsigned
Late 18th/early 19th century

N253
Cluster of five Mushrooms

Wood
Unsigned
Early 19th century

N254
Fruits

Brass ash tray netsuke
Unsigned, style of Karamono Kyubei
18th century

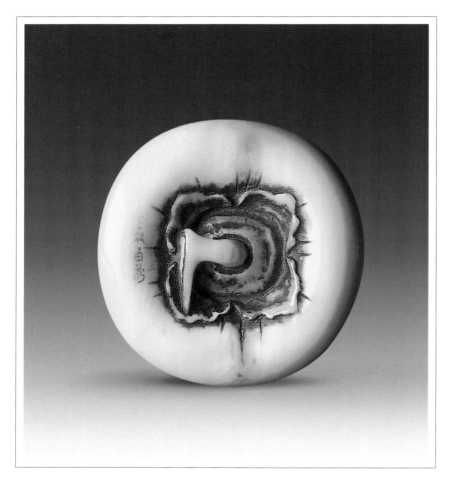

N255
Persimmon *(Kaki)* with stem

Ivory
Signed *Unsho Hakuryu*
Kyoto, 19th century

The carver was Unsho Hakuryu I, identified mainly by the signature, which is engraved in delicate *sosho* script in an irregular reserve. The signature of the second Hakuryu and followers was engraved with much bolder strokes, generally in a gourd-shaped reserve. The work is very similar to examples of the same subject by Mitsuhiro of Osaka.

N256
Cluster of Winter Cherries
(Hozuki)

Wood
Unsigned
Tamba, early 19th century

Provenance:
Cecil Crookes collection

The *hozuki,* variously known in the west as Chinese lanterns, winter cherries or lantern cherries, are a popular delicacy in Japan and China.

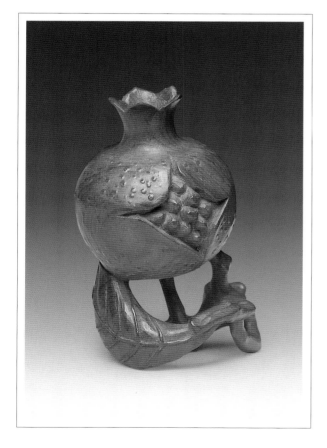

N257
Pomegranate *(Zakuro)*

Boxwood
Unsigned
19th century

N258
Two Ojime, each in the form of a Loquat (*Biwa*)

Ivory with horn calyx
Signed *Mitsuhiro* (Ohara Mitsuhiro)
Osaka, 19th century

N259
Bamboo (*Take*)

Ivory
Signed *Mitsuhiro,* with seal *Ohara*
Osaka, 19th century

A simple sliver of ivory, fashioned as a section of bamboo, engraved in *katakiri* and *kebori* with wind-blown feathery bamboo leaves.

N260
Bamboo

Ivory
Signed *Mitsuhiro* with
seal *Ohara*
Osaka, 19th century

N261
Bamboo Node

Black and *tan* lacquered wood
Signed *Hashi-ichi* (Hashimoto Hashi-ichi)
Edo (Tokyo), mid to late 19th century

The wood is decorated in typical Hashi-ichi style
to resemble bamboo, with three small ants applied in
black lacquer

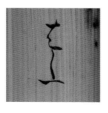

N262
Chestnut *(Kuri)* with worm

Wood, the worm of ivory
Signed *Minko* (Tanaka Minko)
Tsu, late 18th century

A trick netsuke, in that the worm is movable
within a hole in the chestnut.

N263
Chestnut

Wood
Signed *Masanao*
Ise, 19th century

N264
Chestnut

Wood with inlaid ivory
Signed *Kyusai*
Osaka, early 20th century

N265
Ginkgo Nuts

Ivory
Signed *Masamitsu*
19th century

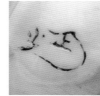

N266
Trailing Chrysanthemums

Hirado ware porcelain
Marked with auspicious characters
19th century

N267
Clouds

Kagamibuta of stag antler and
cloisonné enamel
Unsigned
19th century

N268
Geometric Design

Woven copper wire
Unsigned
19th century

N269
Boar's Tusk

Devoid of decoration
Signed *Iwami ju Kanman*
Iwami, c.1800

The tusk is uncarved and unpolished, save for a polished area to one side that bears the impeccably engraved inscription.

The Inro are basically arranged in chronological order. It should be stated that the question of attribution is often unanswerable, as it was common in Japanese schools of art for successors or apprentices to adopt (with permission) their master's name. Where it is clear, we have cited by which of the successive generations the particular inro was made or designed. In many cases, however, it is virtually impossible to determine this, so we have judged each piece on style and dated it as we see fit.

Inro

IN1
Four-case Lacquer Inro

Unsigned
Possibly Momoyama period
(1568–1615)

Flowering chrysanthemum *(kiku)* in
takamakie and *aogai* on a ground of
fine *nashiji* overlacquered with
feathery fronds in *hiramakie;* the
interior and risers are of fine *nashiji.*

Ojime: carved black lacquer
(tsuikoku) with floral and
ho-o bird designs

Netsuke: two-part *manju* of gold
lacquer, in the form of a
kiku bloom, the interior is
of nashij; unsigned

IN2
Three-case Lacquer and Metal Inro

Unsigned
17th century

A large *shakudo* dragon inlaid among clouds in a mottled gold lacquer pattern on a black ground, the cord runners formed by metal loops; the interior is of *nashiji* with *fundame* rims.

Ojime: metal cylinder with a band of flying birds in silver and *shakudo* on a ground of *karakusa*

Netsuke: a lacquered clam, with dragon design in red and gold *takamakie* on an incised olive green ground; unsigned

IN3
Three-case Lacquer and Metal Inro

Unsigned
17th century

A three-clawed storm dragon, in silvered metal, among swirling clouds over agitated water, on a ground of *fundame* over black lacquer with details of *kirigane,* the cord runners of scalloped metal; the interior is of thick *nashiji.*

Ojime: gilt metal and *sentoku,* Kiyohime coiled around the bell of Dojoji

Netsuke: *kagamibuta* with *shibuichi* disc with a *ho-o* bird in relief over *kiri* blossoms, the bowl of fundame lacquer; unsigned

IN4
Four-case Lacquer Inro

Unsigned
17th century

A farmer running after an ox that rests to graze beneath a pine tree, in gold and black *hiramakie* with details of *kirigane*, the farmer and ox inlaid with tortoiseshell; the interior is of pale *nashiji*, the shoulders and rims of *fundame*.

Ojime: horn, cylinder bearing a working compass
Netsuke: agate perfume bottle of double gourd form with applied silver *kiku* bloom and loose ring *himotoshi*; unsigned

IN5
Four-case Lacquer Inro

Signed *Sotetsu, nana-ju-ni sai* (at the age of 72)
1689

A pine branch in gold *togidashi-e* passing over one case only, on a ground of rich *roiro*, the cord runners with foliate design in *karakusa* style, in gold *hiramakie;* the interior is of gold *nashiji* with rims of *fundame.*

Ojime: coral, carved as a dragon
Netsuke: lacquer *manju,* with a design of blossoms and leaves in *takamakie* and *e-nashiji* on a *roiro* ground; signed *Kansai*

IN6
Three-case Lacquer Inro

Signed *Ritsuo* (Ogawa Haritsu)
Probably early 18th century

In the form of an old Chinese ink cake, with a design of musical instruments and auspicious objects around the edge; one side with young ferns *(warabi)* in pewter, green and gold glazed pottery and *aogai,* the other side with two large characters reading *Gueon chein;* the interior is of black lacquer, the shoulders and rims of *fundame.*

Ojime: grooved cylindrical wood bead
Netsuke: *manju* in the form of a *kagamibuta,* the fluted black lacquer bowl encircling a design of warabi in pewter and *raden*; signed *Issai*

Provenance:
S.Bing collection, no. 124

Published:
Alain Ducros, *Netsuke et Sagemono,* 1987, no. 212
Japanese Lacquer From Southern California Collections, Pacific Asia Museum, 1991, p.19.

Exhibited:
Pasadena, California, 1991

IN7
Four-case Lacquer Inro

Signed on an inlaid green pottery seal *Kan* (Ogawa Haritsu)

A large falcon clutching a captured heron within its talons, inlaid in white glazed pottery, among grasses in greenish-black lacquer and forget-me-nots *(ruriso)* in blue glazed pottery with gold lacquer foliage; the reverse with a heron flying over a meandering stream, all on a *tsugaru-nuri* ground; the interior is of fine gold *nashiji,* the shoulders and rims of *fundame.* The design on both sides represents a tragic scene, the female heron being ferociously attacked by the falcon, while her mate screams as he flies away on the reverse.

Ojime: two bats in Negoro lacquer with gold details
Netsuke: solid Negoro lacquer *manju,* with a *karyobinga* (human-faced bird) holding two lotus buds, an elongated water dragon on the reverse, unsigned

IN8
Single-case Inro

Unsigned, style of Tsuchida Soetsu
18th century

Of broad form, with a design of six plovers *(chidori)* flying over a formalised bridge, inlaid with *raden* and *aogai* on a brown ground; the interior of brown lacquer with rims of *fundame*.

Ojime: agate bead
Netsuke: wood *katabori* figure of Fukurokuju;
                unsigned

Provenance:
Demaree and Dorothy Bess collection
Charles A. Greenfield collection

Published:
Pekarick, *Japanese Lacquer, 1600–1900,* no. 57, fig. 71

Exhibited:
The Magnificent Three, New York 1972, no. 17
Metropolitan Museum of Art, New York, 1980
Eskenazi, Ltd., London, 1990, no. 57

IN9
Single-case Wood and Lacquer Inro

Unsigned
Early 18th century

Of rounded square form with an openwork fluted rim and surmounted by a Chinese pagoda-style roof, the body with square cartouches on either side, of red lacquer, with designs of a *kirin* and *ho-o* bird in variously toned *aogai,* the curved rim of the cover inlaid with aogai in geometric patterns.

Ojime: *guri* lacquer, deeply carved with
              tasselled symbols
Netsuke: *manju simulating a kagamibuta,* of
                cypress wood, the fluted wood bowl
                lacquered reddish brown, bearing a
                disc carved and lacquered with a
                writhing dragon; unsigned

The inro was almost certainly made in the Ryukyu islands by Chinese workers, for the Japanese market

IN10
Four-case Lacquer Inro

Unsigned
Early 18th century

Seashells among various aquatic plants, in gold and black lacquer on a rubbed gold and black ground with a scattering of *kirigane,* the top and bottom sprinkled with *nashiji;* the interior is of nashiji with *fundame* rims, each case with *kanji,* presumably denoting the medicine contained.

Ojime: ivory bead with inlaid designs

Netsuke: rectangular *manju* of wood, inlaid and lacquered with two pottery shells and a crab amid seaweed; signed on a green pottery tablet *Naoyuki*

IN11
Small Three-case Inro

Signed *Jokasai*
Probably early 18th century

Bearing a *roiro* ground and decorated in *yamimakie* with stone lanterns among cryptomeria and pine trees at the Kasuga shrine in Nara, one side showing two seated *sika* deer in brown lacquer with silver spots; the interior of pale gold *nashiji,* the shoulders and rims of *fundame.*

Ojime: coral bead
Netsuke: peach, in dark wood; signed *Takusai* (Tategawa or Tachikawa Takusai)

IN12
Large Five-case Lacquer Inro

Unsigned.
18th century

Raiden reaching for his circle of thunder drums and holding a drum stick as he flees from a dog that ferociously bites his ankle, bolts of lightning amid clouds above, the design continued on the reverse, all in gold, silver and brown *takamakie* and *hiramakie* on a *roiro* ground; the interior is of *nashiji,* the shoulders and rims of *fundame.*

Ojime: wood bead
Netsuke: *kagamibuta* of wood with brass disc bearing a demon mask in relief; unsigned

IN13
Small Four-case Lacquer Inro

Unsigned
18th century

A continuous scene of a spreading pine tree, in gold *takamakie*, beside a Chinese style formal terrace in *aogai* with details inlaid in pewter and carefully aligned sections of mother-of-pearl, all on a *roiro* ground; the interior is of matt black lacquer, the shoulders and rims of *fundame*.

Ojime: coral bead
Netsuke: *kagamibuta,* the ivory bowl bearing a disc of *shibuichi* engraved with grasses and leaves in *katakiri* and *kebori,* beneath the crescent moon inlaid with silver; unsigned

IN14
Single-case Lacquer Inro

Unsigned
18th century

A large four-pronged anchor, inlaid in *raden,* with a gold lacquer rope, the reverse with delicate water plants in gold *hiramakie* and inlaid pewter; the interior contains a shelf compartment, black lacquered with *fundame* rims.

Ojime: silver gilt bead applied with two copper crabs

Netsuke: *kagamibuta,* the bowl of walrus tusk, bearing a *sentoku* disc, inlaid with a crab in silver and *shakudo;* unsigned

Provenance:
Roberta Pincus collection

IN15
Four-case Lacquer Inro

Unsigned
18th century

Seven *karako* in a Chinese dragon boat on water, with cloud bands above, the design continued on the reverse, in gold and coloured *takamakie* and *hiramakie* with *kirigane* and inlaid *aogai* details, on a ground of *roiro* with scattered *mura-nashiji;* the interior is of gold *nashiji,* the shoulders and rims of *fundame.*

Ojime: coral bead
Netsuke: ivory, a boy seated holding a winter cherry *(hozuki),* the fruit inlaid with coral; signed *Masayuki*

The design is based on a double-page spread in *Ehon Jikishiko,* by Tachibana Morikuni, 1745.

IN16
Four-case Lacquer Inro

Unsigned
18th century

The narrow ribbed surface with a design of hare's foot ferns *(shinobu),* a tiny grasshopper to one side, in painted orange-red lacquer on a *roiro* ground; the interior of *nashiji.*

Ojime: coral bead
Netsuke: asymmetrical bamboo section fitted with a gold lacquered disc inlaid with three cherry blossoms in gold, silver and coral on a lacquered *gyobu* ground; unsigned

IN17
Three-case Lacquer Inro

Signed in seal form *Shiomi Masanari*
18th century

A large butterfly inlaid in tortoiseshell with a large *tsuishu* lacquer dragonfly on the reverse, amid a riotous display of flowering plants in coloured mother-of-pearl and pewter with gold lacquer foliage, all on a matt black ground; the interior is of black lacquer, decorated with gold lacquered geometric patterns.

Ojime: lacquered wood bead, carved with dragonflies
Netsuke: *kagamibuta,* the stag-antler bowl with a *cloisonné* enamel disc with a floral design; unsigned

IN18
Four-case Lacquer Inro

Signed *Shiomi Masanari*
Probably 18th century

Design of a torii in *togidashi-e,* rising amid a forest of cryptomeria trees in gold *hiramakie* on a mottled tortoiseshell ground (originally black lacquer, made with iron filings); the interior is of reddish *nashiji,* the shoulders and risers of *fundame.*

Ojime: metal, frog on a lotus leaf
Netsuke: two-piece lacquer *manju* with a design of a large camellia and foliage in gold and silver *takamakie* on a brown ground; signed *Yoyusai*

IN19
Large Five-case Lacquer Inro

Unsigned, style of Shiomi Masanari
Probably late 18th century

A large boar asleep among autumn grasses and flowers, in gold *takamakie* on a *roiro* ground, with some sprinkled *nashiji,* and tiny silver dew drops scattered over the entire design. The reverse shows a profusion of Autumn plants and the full moon, which is depicted in silver *togidashi-e;* the interior is of gold nashiji, the shoulders and rims of *fundame.*

Ojime: small black lacquer bead with foliage in gold *hiramakie*
Netsuke: ivory, running boar; signed *Okakoto*

Published:
Kurstin and Ortega, Masterworks of Netsuke, no. 104
NK, vol. 7, no. 2, p. 21, fig. 2

IN20
Five-case Lacquer Inro

Signed *Koma Kyuhaku*
18th century

Moso walking amid snow, carrying bamboo shoots, his head hidden beneath his straw hat, in *takamakie* and *hiramakie* on a rich *nashiji* ground. A snow-laden stand of bamboo is shown on the reverse, the snow depicted in thick silver lacquer; the interior is of red-gold *nashiji,* the shoulders and rims of *fundame.*

Ojime: stag antler square bead carved with a key fret design
Netsuke: wood, two bamboo shoots; signed *Tomokazu*

Provenance:
Baron Takei collection, no. 7B9
Robert Segal collection

Moso (Meng Tsung) was one of the twenty-four Chinese paragons of filial piety, who, in winter, went out to dig bamboo shoots for his sick mother. In spite of the fact that they were out of season and the ground was very hard, fine shoots magically appeared at his feet, to his great delight.

IN21
Three-case Lacquer Inro

Signed *Koma Kyuhaku saku*
Late 18th/early 19th century

A flying crane, in silver *takazogan,* its wings spreading onto the reverse, above piled clouds of gold *togidashi-e;* the interior is of matt gold lacquer.

Ojime: amber-colored glass
Netsuke: walrus ivory, Ryusa-style *manju* inlaid in silver with a *ho-o* bird, among foliage and clouds; signed *Mitsuhiro*

IN22
Three-case Lacquer Inro

Signed *Koma Yasuaki*
18th century

Large heavy inro with a continuous design of eleven fish and a lobster, in gold and silver *togidashi-e* on a tan ground with patches of *nashiji,* the interior is of red lacquer with gold rims, the risers decorated with waves in gold and silver-black *togidashi-e.*

Ojime: a round hardstone with orange discs
Netsuke: *manju* type, a large carp in mother-of-pearl on a ground of sea weed in gold lacquer on a scattered nashiji ground; signed with the seal *Chohei*

IN23
Two-case Lacquer Inro

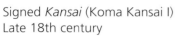

Signed *Kansai* (Koma Kansai I)
Late 18th century

Random over-all design of *kirimon* in *yamamakie,* inlaid on both sides with seven swallows, a kingfisher and a Canada goose, in *raden* and translucent horn; the interior is of *gyobu-nashiji,* the shoulders and rims of *fundame.*

Ojime: ivory, inlaid with three plovers *(chidori)* in translucent horn and raden; signed on a mother-of-pearl reserve *Hozan*
Netsuke: dentine ivory, small bird perched on a head of millet; unsigned

IN24
Metal Three-case Saya Inro

Signed *Yasuchika*
Nara, early 18th century

The *saya* is of *shibuichi*, inlaid in *takazogan* and partly pierced with a night watchman carrying a lantern and umbrella as he passes a *torii* in a slanting rain storm, the reverse with a stone lantern among tall trees, variously inlaid in *shakudo* with details in brass and gilt metal, the rain partly incised and partly inlaid with gold; the inner *otoshi* is of plain silver.

Ojime: shakudo, pea pod bursting open to show a gold pea within

Netsuke: *kagamibuta,* with wood bowl bearing a shibuichi disc with Daruma in relief, in gold and shakudo; signed *Minjo* with *kakihan*

The inro is possibly by Tsuchiya Yasuchika II

IN25
Four-case Tortoiseshell (Bekko) Inro

Unsigned
18th century

Carved on one side in relief with Bishamon in hot pursuit of a large *oni* fleeing with a sacred *stupa,* seen on the reverse among swirling clouds, all on a carved diapered background, over *kanagai* gold foil.

Ojime: carnelian bead
Netsuke: wood *katabori* netsuke of an oni kneeling in clouds and holding a pagoda-shaped shrine; unsigned

Provenance:
Oscar Raphael collection

Published:
H.L. Joly and K. Tomita, *Japanese Art and Handicraft,* no. 163, illus. Pl. LXXXVIII

Exhibited:
London, October-November 1915

IN26
Small Four-case Lacquer Inro

Unsigned
Late 18th century

Several insects, including butterfly, beetle, grasshopper, dragonfly, cricket, mantis and wasp, amid dense vegetation of autumn grasses and flowers, all in gold *togidashi-e* and black and brown *hiramakie* on a *roiro* ground with sprinkled *kimpun*, the interior of *gyobu*, the shoulders and rims of *fundame*.

Ojime: metal ovoid
Netsuke: black lacquered wood, peapod with a grasshopper and bee lacquered in gold hiramakie; signed *Kozan*

Published:
NK, vol. 7, no. 2, p. 23, fig. 8

IN27
Four-case Lacquer Inro

Signed *Jokasai*
Late 18th/early 19th century

Densely patterned design of trees in gold and black *takamakie* on a black and gold ground of stylised wave design, between bands of cloud in *fundame*, details of metallic silver, gold and *aogai kirigane* on the flowering branches; the interior is of *nashiji*.

Ojime: gold lacquer, with a design of lotus plants, details of coral
Netsuke: black lacquered *tabako-ire,* complete with *kiseru,* netsuke, ojime and cords, details of ivory, gold and coral; signed *Ekizan*

IN28
Four-case Lacquer Inro

Signed *Jokasai*
Late 18th/early 19th century

Two large carp swimming among sea grasses and seaweed, in gold and silver *takamakie*, with details of *hiramakie* and *togidashi-e*, their eyes inlaid, on a ground of *mura-nashiji*; the interior is of dense red-gold *nashiji*.

Ojime: amber bead
Netsuke: dried truncated fish in ray-skin, lacquer and horn; unsigned

Published:
Chappell and Welch: *Netsuke, The Japanese Art of Miniature Carving*, no. 195 (netsuke only)

Exhibited:
Minneapolis, April-July 1998

IN29
Four-case Lacquer Inro

Signed *Chohei* with kakihan
18th century

A fox dressed as a priest, standing and holding a *hossu* beside a flowering chrysanthemum *(kiku);* the reverse with a hunter wearing camouflage and hiding behind a rice stook, the fox of gold, silver and black *takamakie,* its face and feet in *raden,* the hunter of thick raden with ivory face, other details in takamakie, *hiramakie* and mother-of-pearl, all on a dark brown ground; the interior is of *nashiji,* the shoulders of *fundame.*

Ojime: ivory, three-faced mask
Netsuke: *kagamibuta,* the gold lacquered bowl bearing a metal disc, showing a *bakemono* with flames issuing from its mouth, frightening a *tengu,* lacquered and inlaid with pottery; signed *Teiji*

IN30
Single-case Wood and Lacquer Inro

Signed with the seal of *Chohei*
Late 18th century

The wood ground is covered with a netting design in dark brown lacquer, that stretches over the top and bottom, decorated with tea ceremony *(cha-no-yu)* utensils in various techniques, including a tea bowl *(chawan)* of glazed pottery, with a camellia in gold and red lacquer and *aogai,* a spoon *(chashaku)* in gold lacquer, a feather *(haboku)* in black lacquer, and a tripod to support the kettle *(gotoku)* in black *sabejinuri;* the interior has risers decorated with peonies and *karakusa* in red, green and gold *hiramakie* on a black ground, the shoulders and rims of dark brown lacquer.

Ojime: ivory, small pulley used to haul the kettle from the fire, which is lowered into the ground in winter
Netsuke: wood, teakettle *(kama)* with loose lid and open handles, carved with a design of *kiku* and foliage; unsigned

IN31
Large Three-case Lacquer Inro

Signed *Kajikawa Tomohide*
Late 18th/early 19th century

A large crane in *tsuishu* lacquer, flying among falling plum blossoms in gold *takamakie* and foil, the design continuing on the reverse, all on a *rogin-nuri* ground with a slight dusting of gold powder; the interior of red lacquer, the risers of *nashiji* and the shoulders and rims of *fundame*.

Ojime: tsuishu lacquer bead carved with a rooster and hen among wheat sheaves and flowering shrubs on a diaper ground

Netsuke: wood *hako-netsuke* with cover design of a heron in gold *hiramakie,* with a red lacquer seal; signed *Hoitsu ga, Gyokuzan* (by Gyokuzan, after the design by [Sakai] Hoitsu)

Published:
Japanese Lacquer From Southern California Collections, Pacific Asia Museum, 1991, p.24
Kurstin and Ortega, *Masterworks of Netsuke*, no. 105

Exhibited:
Pasadena, California, 1991

IN32
Four-case Lacquer Inro

Signed *Tatsuke Takanori*
Late 18th/early 19th century

Five *No* and *Kyogen* masks, comprising those of *karasu tengu, konoha tengu,* Saruta hito, Okame and Hannya, in high relief gold and coloured *takamakie* with slight *aogai* details, on a ground of *mura-nashiji;* the interior is of gold *nashiji* with *fundame* rims.

Ojime: *tsuishu* lacquer, masks of Okame and O-Beshimi

Netsuke: gold lacquered wood, mask of O-Tenjin; signed *Kajikawa*

IN33
Single-case Lacquer Inro

Signed *Toshi with kakihan*
Late 18th/early 19th century

A *ginseng* plant continuing over both sides, in gold *takamakie* with *hiramakie* roots and inlaid coral berries, on a ground of *roiro* with sprinkled *hirame;* the interior is of rich brown-red *nashiji,* the shoulders and rims of *fundame,* containing three shaped medicine bottles.

Ojime: coral bead
Netsuke: wood, group of three mushrooms, lacquered gold on the top; unsigned

IN34
Three-case Wood Inro

Signed *Togi* with *kakihan*
Late 18th/early 19th century

Two geese flying down towards wind-blown reeds, in gold, silver and black *takamakie;* the interior of dark brown lacquer, the shoulders and rims of *fundame.*

Ojime: *sentoku,* inlaid with irises in silver.

Netsuke: stained stag antler, a lotus leaf, curled at the edges and with a metal ring cord attachment; signed *Koku* (sai)

IN35
Four-case Lacquer Inro

Unsigned
Late 18th/early 19th century

Two large crabs among various shells and seaweed, in gold, silver and red *hiramakie* and *slight takamakie* on a matt black ground; the interior contains fitted ivory inserts, each in the form of a *shunga* scene, three of a man and woman, one of a woman wielding a *harikata*.

Ojime: ivory, monkey climbing a rope

Netsuke: lacquer *manju,* with a formal design in *guri-bori;* unsigned

IN36
Three-case Lacquer Inro

Unsigned
Late 18th/early 19th century

An mendicant priest's travelling case *(oi)*, resting among vines and trailing ivy, before distant hills, the oi of inlaid pewter with *aogai* and lacquer details, the leaves of gold lacquer, pewter, *shibuichi* and mother-of-pearl, while the three conical mountains are of barely outlined *togidashi-e*, all on a rich *roiro* ground; the interior is of brown-black lacquer.

Ojime: *shakudo* cylinder, inlaid with blossoms in silver and brass; signed *Ikko*

Netsuke: small lacquer *hako,* with three stylised birds in pewter, *aogai* and coloured lacquer on a roiro ground; unsigned

The subject refers to the Mount Utsu episode from the epic story, Tales from Ise *(Ise Monogatari)* and is the subject of a poem by Ariwara no Narihira.

IN37
Two-case Inro of Reishi Fungus

Signed *Kokei* with *kakihan* and seal
Late 18th/early 19th century

A *tanuki* seated, beating its stomach, beside rocks, a tree trunk and grasses beneath the crescent moon, all inlaid in wood, *raden, umimatsu* and silver.

Ojime: *sentoku,* inlaid with silver cherry blossoms and scattered petals; signed *Masayuki*
Netsuke: wood, tanuki seated beating its distended stomach; signed *Minko*

IN38
Four-case Wood Inro

Signed *Kokei* with *kakihan*
Late 18th/early 19th century

A *tanuki* seated, drumming its stomach, beside rocks and a tree trunk among grasses, beneath the crescent moon, a stream on the reverse.

Ojime: glass bead
Netsuke: none

IN39
Four-case Lacquer Inro

Signed *Ritsuo* with seal *Kan*
Probably early 19th century

Design of an old Chinese ink cake, the sides and edges with simulated chips and cracks, imitating the old worn ink, one side decorated with a scene from a painting, depicting Kan'u with an attendant, in gold, silver and slight coloured *takamakie* on a *kinji* ground; the reverse with a panel of six characters in relief, reading: "Ink of the great collection of painting classics"; the interior is of black lacquer with silver rims.

Ojime: black and white glass
Netsuke: wood and lacquer *manju,* in the form of an alms bowl containing a *mokugyo* and a rubbed ink cake, signed *Koma Kansai* (after the idea of Ritsuo)

Provenance:
The inro is from the Corbin and the Baron Takei collections

Published:
NK, vol. 7, no. 2, p. 22, fig. 7
S.L. Moss, Ltd., *Eccentrics in Netsuke,* no. 3
The inro was almost certainly made after Ritsuo's design, and produced at a later date.

IN40
Two-case Wood Inro

Signed, on pottery seal, *Kan*
19th century

A standing deer, seen from the rear, inlaid in beige, white and brown pottery, the reverse with a dove seated on a *torii* among wild flowers, details in brown lacquer.

Ojime: small metal bell; signed on a ceramic plaque *Kenya*

Netsuke: wood, square *manju,* inlaid with Buddhist symbols in pottery and pewter; signed on a ceramic plaque *Kenya*

Provenance:

F.P. Schneider collection

The inro was acquired by Virginia Atchley with the netsuke and ojime already in place. It is likely that all three were made by Kenya, after a design by Ogata Korin in the typical Rimpa tradition.

IN41
Three-case Lacquer Inro

Unsigned, style of Ogata Korin
Probably 19th century

Design of irises in the Rimpa manner, in *takamakie,* inlaid with pewter and mother-of-pearl on a ground of dark brown lacquer, sprinkled with gold flecks; the interior is of fine *nashiji,* the risers of *fundame.*

Ojime: dulled gold metal, moulded with a teabowl *(chawan)* and tea whisk *(chasen)*

Netsuke: *manju* of oval form, lacquered in gold and brown with a design of paulownia *(kiri)* blossoms and leaves; unsigned

IN42
Four-case Lacquer Inro

Signed *Shoryusai Tatsuei* with seal
Late 18th/early 19th century

A battle scene, showing mounted warriors riding out into the shallows against an enemy fleet, all in gold, silver and black *togidashi-e* with details in *hiramakie, kirigane* and *e-nashiji*, on a ground of *kinji;* the interior is of red-gold *nashiji,* the shoulders and rims of *fundame*

Ojime: small globular bead, lacquered in fundame
Netsuke: ivory, helmet *(kabuto);* unsigned

The scene is a reference to the battle of Yashima between the Taira and Minamoto clans, in 1185.

IN43
Four-case Lacquer Inro

Signed *Chikanao*
19th century

In the form of a bird cage, containing three quail, in gold and silver *hiramakie* on an orange lacquer ground; the bars of the cage in gold lacquer, and the base, supported on four bracket feet, bears a brocade pattern in Somada style, with informal medallions of dragons and clouds in *takamakie,* the bottom of gold *hirame;* the interior is of gold *nashiji,* the risers of *fundame.*

Ojime: coral bead
Netsuke: ivory, two quail with a fledgling on millet heads; inscribed *Okatomo*

Published:

Kurstin and Ortega, *Masterworks of Netsuke,* no. 107
NK, vol. 7, no. 2, p. 21, fig. 4

IN44
Five-case Lacquer Inro

Signed *Bushu ju Kajikawa zo* (Made by Kajikawa, living in Buzen (province)) with seal
19th century

Rosei's dream of greatness, in gold and coloured *takamakie* and *togidashi-e*, with inlays of *aogai* and horn, and details of *kirigane* on a rich *roiro* ground, Rosei reclining on a bench beneath a pine tree dreaming of being carried in a procession that is shown on the reverse in delicate togidashi-e; the interior is of *nashiji,* the shoulders and rims of *fundame.*

Ojime: carnelian bead
Netsuke: black lacquered wood, Daikoku's treasure sack, inlaid with six of the *takaramono* in ivory, coral, mother-of- pearl and lacquer; unsigned

Rosei (Chao lu Sheng) was a poor man who travelled to the capital to become a councillor to the emperor. On the way, he lay down to sleep and dreamt of becoming a great man surrounded by a retinue of attendants. The well-known story was later adapted as a *No* play in Japan (see also S15)

IN45
Three-case Lacquer Inro

Signed *Kajikawa saku*
19th century

Various aquatic creatures, including whale and crayfish, octopus and flat fish, in gold, silver, red and green *takamakie*, with details of *aogai*, on a rich *okibirame* ground; the interior is of orange-gold *gyobu-nashiji*, the shoulders and rims of *fundame*.

Ojime: coral bead
Netsuke: ivory, catfish *(namazu)* with gourd, referring to the story of Kadori Myojin; signed *Shunkosai* (Chogetsu)

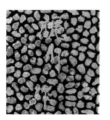

IN46
Four-case Lacquer Inro

Signed *Kajikawa saku*
19th century

Two fat rabbits among grasses and small flowers, including orchid, *hagi* and young pines, in gold *takamakie* with details of *kirigane* on a *kinji* ground; the interior is of fine *nashiji*, the shoulders and rims of *fundame*.

Ojime: carved coral
Netsuke: two-piece ivory *manju*, with two seated rabbits, one incised in *sumie*, beside a clump of *tokusa* grass; signed *Tadachika*

IN47
Small Two-case Lacquer Inro

Signed *Yoshioka zu, Kajikawa utsusu kore* (Kajikawa copied from a design by Yoshioka) 19th century

A presentation ball of flowers (*kusadama*), with trailing ribbons, the design continuing onto the reverse, all in gold *hiramakie* on a dark brown ground; the interior is of red-gold *nashiji*, the shoulders and rims of *fundame*.

Ojime: green glass bead
Netsuke: ivory, Hotei crawling through his treasure sack; signed *Ikkosai* (Toun)

IN48
Four-case Lacquer Inro

Signed *Kajikawa Bunryusai,* with red *tsubo* seal
19th century

A fox disguised as a woman, holding a cane, standing among autumn plants, a field mouse caught in a trap to one side, all richly depicted in gold and slight *takamakie* with profuse use of *kirigane* and *e-nashiji,* the trunk of a tree to one side, with boles and knot holes in *uchikomi;* the interior is of red lacquer with *nashiji* risers, the shoulders and rims of *fundame;* on the underside of the top case is the name of the medicine to be contained.

Ojime: brass and silver covered pot; signed *Ichiyusai*

Netsuke: lacquered wood fox head, of brown lacquer with details of gold lacquer and kirigane, the underside of nashiji; unsigned

Published:
NK, vol. 7, no. 2, p. 22, no. 6

IN49
Four-case Lacquer Inro

Signed *Kajikawa Bunryusai, gyonen rokuju-o* (at the age of 60) with *kakihan*
19th century

A night scene at the height of a thunderstorm; two porters carrying a dignitary in a palanquin *(norimono)* are so unnerved when lightning strikes that they drop the norimono, spilling the passenger, who is revealed in the flash of lightning, all in *yamimakie*, gold, red and black *togidashi-e* and *hiramakie*, on a *roiro* ground; the interior is of rich gold *nashiji*.

Ojime: cylindrical drum form with gilt flowers in relief
Netsuke: wood, Raiden astride a thunder drum with storm winds issuing from a double gourd; signed with a *kakihan*

Provenance:

W.W. Winkworth collection
Demaree and Dorothy Bess collection
Charles A. Greenfield collection

Published:

Stern, *The Magnificent Three*, no. 142

Exhibited:

New York, 1972

IN50
Four-case Lacquer Inro

Signed with a *Kajikawa* seal
19th century

The rats' wedding, showing a procession of twenty-seven rats in *yamamakie,* some carrying musical instruments, polearms and banners in gold *hiramakie* with slight coloured details; the interior is of gold *nashiji,* the shoulders and rims of *fundame.*

Ojime: coral bead
Netsuke: black lacquered wood, *shishi* on base; unsigned

IN51
Four-case Lacquer Inro

Signed *Kanshosai*
19th century

An *ukiyo-e* design of courtesans and companions scurrying for cover as they are caught in a sudden wind-whipped thunderstorm, in gold and coloured *togidashi-e,* with details of kirigane, the travellers' *kimono* are covered with delicate gold lacquer designs and the wall of the gate under which they seek cover is of *mokume,* all on a *roiro* ground; the interior of *fundame.*

Ojime: carved stag antler
Netsuke: a *kagamibuta,* the stag antler bowl with green-stained stag antler disc, with a gold lacquered flower design; unsigned

Provenance:
H. Seymour Trower collection, no. 950, illus in the catalogue, pl. XIII

Published:
Beatrice von Rague, *Iizuka Toyo,* no. 274
Alain Ducros, *Netsuke et Sagemono,* 1987, no. 229
Japanese Lacquer from Southern California Collections, pp. 20–21

Exhibited:
Pasadena, California, 1991

The design is taken from a painting by Nishikawa Sukenobu (1671–1750).

IN52
Five-case Lacquer Inro

Signed *Toju, gyonen shichiju o* (at the age of 70) with red *kakihan*
19th century

Five black crows perched on flowering branches, before a large silver moon, in grey
and black *togidashi-e* on a ground of *rogin-nuri;* the interior is of bright *nashiji,* the
shoulders and rims of *fundame,* each case containing a silver metal container with a
rectangular gold strip on each cover for writing the name of the drug it contains.

Ojime:　　silver, with a crow inlaid with *shakudo*
Netsuke:　a *kagamibuta,* the dark wood bowl with silver disc, decorated with three
　　　　　　ravens on a withered branch; unsigned

Provenance:
Helmuth and Madeline Wohlthat collection

Published:
Japanese Lacquer from Southern California Collections, p. 26
NK, Vol. 7, no. 2, p. 23, fig. 13

Exhibited:
Pasadena, California, 1991

The inro design is taken from a painting by Shunboku Ooka (1680–1763), printed
in *Gashi Kaiyoo,* 1751, illustrated in William Anderson, *Pictorial Arts of Japan,* pl.
27 and in Louis Gonse, *l'Art Japonaise,* 1883, vol. 1, pp. 230 and 232.

The *kagamibuta* disc is in the style of the Rinsendo family, who produced a number
of sword fitttings with variations on this design in the 19th century.

IN53
Three-case Lacquer Inro

Signed *Toju, gyonen shichiju o* (at the age of 70) with gold *kakihan* 19th century

Three horses, two on one side, grazing, the other standing with head raised, one of gold *takamakie,* one of brown, rough textured takamakie and the third of dappled *rogin takamakie,* their eyes of horn and teeth of mother-of-pearl, all on an orange over plum coloured ground; the interior is of silver *nashiji,* the shoulders and rims of *fundame,* the top case divided with an opening to contain a fitted square seal.

Ojime: red glass
Netsuke: metal stirrup *(abumi),* of *shakudo* with gilt decoration; signed with a *tensho* seal *Rakushi*

Published:
Alain Ducros, *Netsuke et Sagemono* 1987, No. 244
Kurstin and Ortega, *Masterworks of Netsuke,* no. 106

The design is taken from an original by Kano Morinobu (Tanyu, 1602–1674).

IN54
Five-case Lacquer Inro

Signed *Hasegawa Shigeyoshi* with red *tsubo* seal
19th century

The *rakan* Handaka Sonja, standing and holding his alms bowl from which issues a dragon, inlaid in two shades of gold, the reverse with pine trees, rocks and flowering shrubs by a rushing stream, in gold *takamakie* with details of *kirigane*, on a *kinji* ground, with scattered *mura-nashiji;* the interior is of gold *nashiji,* the risers of nashiji, *rogin-nuri, fundame* and red lacquer, the shoulders and rims of fundame.

Ojime: gold, oval bead with a dragon design
Netsuke: *kagamibuta*, the stag-antler bowl carved with clouds and with a gold disc, cast with Handaka Sonja in relief; the bowl signed *Tokoku*

Published:
Kurstin and Ortega, *Masterworks of Netsuke,* no.108

IN55
Three-case Lacquer Inro

Signed *Shiomi Masanari*
19th century

Three macaques *(macaca fuscata)* as the *sambiki saru,* rendered in unusual swirling *togidashi-e* of gold, red and brown, on a *kinji* ground; the interior is of *roiro* and *fundame.*

Ojime: red coral bead
Netsuke: natural root, orang-utang and child; unsigned

IN56
Four-case Lacquer Inro

Signed *Shiomi Masanari*
19th century

An *oharame*, carrying a basket filled with brushwood and accompanied by a child, is hailed from across a stream by a man, beneath maple trees on either bank, their leaves falling into the stream, all in gold and coloured *togidashi-e* on a *roiro* ground; the interior is of orange-red *nashiji* with *fundame* rims.

Ojime: coral bead

Netsuke: lacquered wood *hako,* with a design of butterflies in gold *hiramakie* with slight coloured and inlaid *aogai* details, on a fundame ground; signed *Gyokusen*

IN57
Two-case Lacquer Inro

Signed *Shunsho* with seal *Kagemasa*
19th century

A ceremonial banner, bearing a *rinzu* design, in gold, silver and red *hiramakie* with cords in gold *takamakie,* the reverse with a dish of *tsuishu* lacquer, supporting a blue-glazed ceramic incense burner with gold cover, all on a *roiro* ground; the interior contains a divided tray, that fits into the compartment, of red lacquer with *fundame* rims.

Ojime: coral bead

Netsuke: tsuishu lacquer, two piece *manju,* carved with the poet Saigyo Hoshi, in silver *takazogan,* with gold details, viewing Mt. Fuji among distant clouds, the reverse with a sage beside a lake; unsigned

Provenance:
F.P. Schneider collection

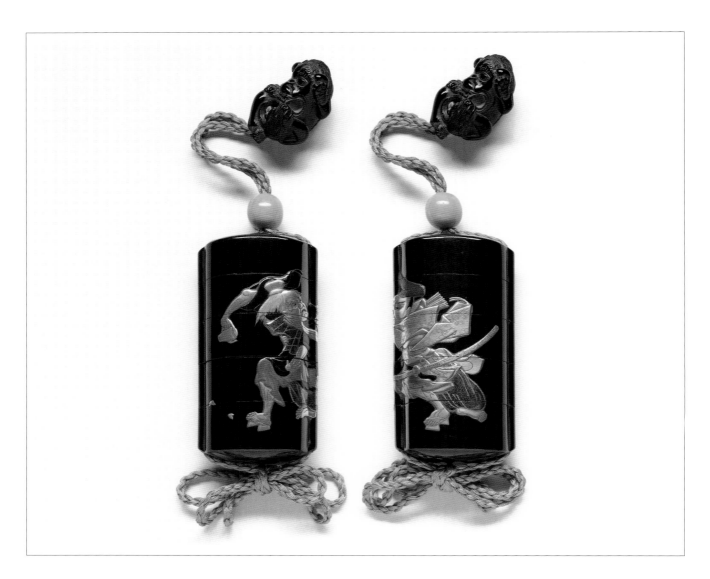

IN58
Four-case Lacquer Inro

Signed *Jokasai*
19th century

Tadamori and the oil thief, the design continued on the reverse, in gold, black and brown *takamakie* with details of *e-nashiji* on a *roiro* ground; the interior of *fundame*.

Ojime: coral bead
Netsuke: black and red painted wood, *bakemono*-style demon; unsigned

Provenance:
Henri Joly collection
Dave Swedlow collection

The design is found on an *ema* tablet, reproduced in *Hengaku Kihan,* illustrated by Aikawa Minwa, 1819.

Taira no Tadamori (1096–1153) was a minor officer of the Imperial Guard of the retired emperor Shirakawa. One night, he paid one his regular visits to the ex-emperor's concubine, and while approaching her abode in a storm, spied a flickering light in the forest. He pounced upon it and found that it was a ragged man who was carrying a flame to light lanterns and to replenish their oil. The raggedly dressed man is often referred to as the thief Abura Bozu, who was stealing the oil. (see also IN72)

IN59
Three-case Lacquer Inro

Signed *Jokasai* with *kakihan*
19th century

A kingfisher flying over grasses and flowers, in gold and coloured *takamakie*, the reverse with a wading heron, inlaid with *raden*, on a *roiro* ground; the interior of black lacquer, incised with *karakusa* in *chinkinbori*.

Ojime: pale coral bead
Netsuke: dentine ivory, formalised kingfisher; signed *Gogetsu*

Published:
The netsuke is illustrated in George Lazarnick, *NIA,* p. 406
NK, vol. 7, no. 2, p. 22, fig. 10

IN60
Four-case Lacquer Inro

Signed *Hokkyo Komin* with *kakihan*
19th century

Raiden and Futen, the former angrily hurling his thunder drums into swirling cloud-filled skies, while his companion disgorges his wind-filled bag, all in gold and coloured *hiramakie* and *takamakie,* the body of Raiden in *shukin* (red-gold), all on a black lacquer ground with gold powder and scattered *nashiji,* the deities' eyes inlaid with horn; the interior is of red-gold nashiji, the shoulders and rims of *fundame.*

Ojime: coral bead
Netsuke: gold over red lacquer, mask of an *oni;* unsigned

IN61
Three-case Lacquer Inro

Unsigned, attributed to Jitokusai Gyokuzan
19th century

A Daruma kite, in gold and coloured *togidashi-e,* the scattered strings in gold *hiramakie* and continuing on the reverse, together with a small gold hawk kite with single string attached to a spool, on a *roiro* ground; the interior of red-gold *nashiji,* the shoulders and rims of *fundame.*

Ojime: copper and *shakudo,* Daruma
Netsuke: *kagamibuta* of rectangular form, the wood bowl with ivory disc, carved in relief with a *Kyogen* mask; unsigned

Published:

Kurstin and Ortega, *Masterworks of Netsuke,* no. 112 (inro only)

IN62
Four-case Lacquer Inro

Signed *Koma Kyuhaku*
19th century

Kintaro holding an *uchiwa* and acting as the referee of a wrestling bout between a monkey and a hare, the reverse with five animals, black bear, deer, badger, squirrel and rabbit, cheering the combatants, all in gold and slightly toned *takamakie* with *aogai* details on a ground of *kinji;* the interior is red lacquer, unusually decorated with childrens' toys in coloured *togidashi-e*.

Ojime: amber bead
Netsuke: wood, Himalayan bear, with an inlaid white crescent at the neck; signed *Minko* (Tanaka Minko)

Kintaro (also known as Kintoki) was a legendary boy, the posthumous child of Sakata Kurando, who was reared by the old mountain woman, Yama Uba. Various stories tell of his great strength and he is often depicted with wild animals and carrying a large felling axe.

IN63
Four-case Lacquer Inro

Signed *Koma Yasutada*
19th century

Two prancing horses, one of *tan* lacquer, with gold mane, tail and fetlocks, black hooves and muzzle, the other of black lacquer sprinkled with gold powder and with gold mane, tail and fetlocks, all on a pale brown ground; the interior having divided compartments of orange lacquer, the risers black and the rims and shoulders of *fundame*.

Ojime: hardstone bead
Netsuke: wood, grazing horse; unsigned

Published:
Japanese Lacquer from Southern California Collections, p. 25

Exhibited:
Pasadena, California, 1991

IN64
Three-case Lacquer Inro

Signed *Koma Koryu saku*, with *kakihan*
19th century

Several half clam shells from the shell game *(kai awase)*, variously lacquered with trees, blossoms and clouds in *takamakie* and *hiramakie*, the reverse of one shown in *rogin-nuri*, all on a rich red-gold *nashiji* ground with scattered *ohirame* in *kanoko* (deer spot) technique; the interior is of red lacquer, the risers, shoulders and rims of *fundame*.

Ojime: coral bead
Netsuke: stag antler, small two piece *manju,* gold lacquered with a
              vine and inlaid with a tiny gold *ho-o* bird and a silver peony
              with foliage; signed in gold lacquer *Kansai*

Kai awase is a game played with three hundred and sixty half clam shells, one half bearing a verse and the other a picture to illustrate the poem. The shells are divided among the players, who alternately throw a valve with a picture, and the verse to which it refers.

IN65
Four-case Lacquer Inro

Signed with scratched characters *Zeshin* (Shibata Zeshin)
19th century

Shoki looking out threateningly from a circular window at a fleeing *oni,* shown on the reverse, all engraved in *katakiri* and *kebori,* one side bearing a grey *ishime* ground, the other side of *roiro* lacquer; the interior is of red-gold *gyobu-nashiji,* the shoulders and rims of *fundame.*

Ojime: green jade
Netsuke: a *kagamibuta,* the black lacquered ivory bowl with *shakudo* disc, bearing a Hannya mask in gold *takazogan;* signed *Yoshihiko*

IN66
Three-case Lacquer Inro

Signed with scratched characters
Zeshin (Shibata Zeshin)
19th century

A spray of flowers tied in a wrapper, in gold and silver *hiramakie,* the reverse with a pine branch in *katakiri* bearing five small pine cones in dark red lacquer, all on a dark green *ishime* ground, simulating algae covered stone; the interior of gold *nashiji,* the shoulders and rims of *fundame.*

Ojime: small coral bead
Netsuke: marine ivory, lotus bud on curling lotus leaf; unsigned

Provenance:

W.W. Winkworth collection
M.T. Hindson collection

IN67
Five-case Lacquer Inro

Signed *Josensai* with *kakihan*
19th century

A branch of double gourds and large leaves in brown, grey and orange *takamakie,* a single blossom with two small buds inlaid in *raden,* the reverse with the *kanji* for *kotobuki* (long life), in *yamamakie;* the interior is of brown-orange *nashiji,* the rims of *fundame.*

Ojime: coral bead
Netsuke: orange lacquered double gourd, with metal cap and ring *himotoshi;* signed *Hashi-ichi*

IN68
Four-case Lacquer Inro

Signed *Josen*
Dated Meiji 2 (1869)

The warrior Ryotoshin (Ch: Li Tong-pin) slaying a large dragon, shown in *chinkinbori,* their eyes inlaid with glass, the *Kaga umebachi-mon* shown on either side in gold *togidashi-e.*

Ojime: agate, oval bead
Netsuke: stag-antler, two-part Ryusa style *manju,* carved and pierced with a slender dragon and seal character among water and lotus leaves; unsigned

IN69
Two-case Wood Inro

Signed *Kyosui zo*
19th century

A love letter vendor *(keso-bumi-uri)* stands, a silk scarf draped over the lower part of his face and wearing a tall hat *(tate-eboshi),* carrying over his shoulder a flowering plum branch, to which are attached three folded love letters, the reverse with a young girl in elaborate attire, holding a battledore and shuttlecock, all in gold, black and red *takamakie* with details of inlaid *aogai.*

Ojime: lacquered wood, vertically striped and with woven gold chain

Netsuke: lacquered ivory, *mikuji bako,* a cylindrical votive box containing three loose ivory wands, the exterior lacquered brown and with an *ema* bearing the words *ho to* (respectfully submitted), among flowering plum blossoms; unsigned

Provenance:
H. Seymour Trower collection, no. 1065
W.H. Behrens collection, no. 365

Published:
NK, vol. 7, no. 2, p. 23, fig. 12

IN70
Four-case Lacquer Inro

Signed *Yoyusai saku* and *Hamano Noriyuki*
19th century

Kikujido seated among flowering chrysanthemums *(kiku)* beside a rushing stream, the figure inlaid in *shakudo* and *shibuichi* with gilt details, the landscape of predominantly gold *takamakie* and *hiramakie* with a profusion of *kirigane* and *e-nashiji* on a *kinji* ground; the interior is of thick gold *nashiji*, the shoulders and rims of *fundame*.

Ojime: black lacquered bead with a gold lacquer foliate design

Netsuke: two part ivory *manju*, carved in *shishiaibori* with Kikujido, holding a chrysanthemum *(kiku)* leaf and writing brush, as he contemplates a poem; signed *Hojitsu*

Kikujido (Keuh Tsze), an attendant of the emperor Muh Wang, was exiled to a valley where he painted the petals of the profuse chrysanthemums that grew there with sacred characters. The dew that washed away his work thence became the elixir of everlasting youth.

IN71
Four-case Lacquer Inro

Signed with a *tensho* seal *Seido* (?)
19th century

A dramatic design of five intertwined geese swooping through the sky, in strips of variously toned mother-of-pearl, their feet, beaks and eyes of black lacquer, all on a ground of densely laid *okibirame* over *kinji;* the interior is of red lacquer with *fundame* rims.

Ojime: carved coral
Netsuke: two piece ivory *manju,* of oval form, inlaid with a bird in *shakudo* with *raden* eye, flying past the mother-of-pearl crescent moon; signed *Doraku* with *kakihan*

Published:
Kurstin and Ortega, *Masterworks of Netsuke,* no. 103

IN72
Four-case Lacquer Inro

Signed *Kirei* (?)
19th century

Tadamori capturing the oil thief, in gold, silver and coloured *hiramakie* on a *roiro* ground, the reverse with two cryptomeria trees in *hakeme* technique, in tones of red and green; the interior is of gold *nashiji*, the shoulders and rims of *fundame*.

Ojime: cloisonné enamel bead, with a snake, baring white fangs
Netsuke: wood, Tadamori capturing the oil thief, the latter with horn eyes;
            signed *Miwa*

Provenance:
Demaree and Dorothy Bess collection
Charles A. Greenfield collection

Published:
Stern, *The Magnificent Three*, no. 128

Exhibited:
Japan House Gallery, New York, 1972

The *hakeme* technique shown here is typified by the actual brush strokes of the lacquer painting clearly shown.

IN73
Three-case Lacquer Inro

Unsigned
19th century

Five *karako* playing beneath a flowering cherry tree, variously dancing, holding a banner, riding a hobbyhorse and playing a drum and trumpet, all in gold and slight coloured *takamakie* and *hiramakie* with details of *e-nashiji*, their faces and other details inlaid in silver, horn, wood, tortoiseshell, stained ivory, coral and *tsuishu* lacquer; the interior is of orange-gold *nashiji,* the risers of *fundame.*

Ojime: coral bead
Netsuke: ivory, two piece square *manju,* carved in *shishiaibori* with a karako carrying a sack; signed *Hojitsu*

The design is taken from *Ehon Jikishino* by Tachibana Morikuni, 1745.

IN74
Four-case Lacquer Inro

Unsigned
19th century

Design of *tagasode* ("whose sleeves?") showing various garments, together with an inro, *kinchaku* and netsuke hanging on a *kimono* rack *(iko),* in *takamakie* and *hiramakie,* beside a partially open screen that continues onto the reverse, painted with a lady at a window gazing at pine trees in moonlight, in gold, silver, black and red *togidashi-e,* all on a brilliant *nashiji* ground; the interior is of nashiji, the risers of *rogin-nuri* and the rims and shoulders of *fundame.*

Ojime: agate oval bead
Netsuke: a *kagamibuta,* the ivory bowl bearing a silver metal disc in the form of a *tsuba,* with an iris engraved in *katakiri* and *kebori;* unsigned

Provenance:
Arthur Kay collection, no. 433

IN75
Six-case Lacquer Inro

Unsigned
19th century

Mountainous landscape, with cherry trees and waterfalls at Yoshino, amid clouds, in gold and silver *takamakie* and *hiramakie* with *kirigane,* all on a *kinji* ground; the interior is of *nashiji,* the shoulders and rims of *fundame,* three cases containing fitted boxes.

Ojime: *sentoku,* of cylindrical form, with inlaid gold and silver blossoms and foliage; signed *Shukoku*

Netsuke: bamboo *manju,* with apollonian *(kiri)* blossoms in gold lacquer; unsigned

Provenance:
Frederick E. Church collection
Charles A. Greenfield collection

Published:
Eskenazi, Ltd., *The Charles A. Greenfield Collection of Inro and Lacquer,* no. 139
Pekarik, *Japanese Lacquer, 1600–1900,* no. 145
Stern, *The Magnificent Three,* no. 26

IN76
Four-case Lacquer Inro

Unsigned
19th century

Bust portrait of Daruma, outlined with inlaid *raden,* the reverse with swaying tree fronds similarly portrayed with outlines of *raden* and oxidised pewter; the interior is of red-gold *gyobu-nashiji,* the shoulders and rims of *fundame.*

Ojime: ivory seated Daruma
Netsuke: wood and lacquer fly switch *(hossu);* unsigned

Published:
Hurtig, *Masterpieces,* no. 7 (netsuke only)
Japanese Lacquer from Southern California Collections, Pacific Asia Museum, p. 27
NK, vol. 7, no. 2, p. 21, fig. 5

Exhibited:
Pasadena, California, 1991

IN77
Four-case Lacquer Inro

Unsigned
19th century

Of oval form, inlaid with seven small flying birds in metal *takazogan,* among wind-blown rice plants and foliage in gold *takamakie* on a ground of sprinkled *aogai;* the interior risers are of orange gold *nashiji* and each compartment is lined with silver.

Ojime: metal, with a bat on either side
Netsuke: copper two-part *manju,* with plovers *(chidori)* flying over waves in relief; unsigned

IN78
Four-case Lacquer Inro

Unsigned
Late 19th century

A quail and two sparrows beneath overhanging millet heads and leaves, inlaid in yellow mother-of-pearl, various shell and painted ivory, on a bright *kinji* ground with scattered *kirigane;* the interior compartments are of dense red-gold *nashiji,* the shoulders and rims of *fundame,* and the risers of nashiji with formal floral designs in gold *togidashi-e.*

Ojime: agate bead
Netsuke: *kagamibuta,* the ivory bowl with a *shakudo* disc, inlaid in silver and gilt metal with a crane flying over millet, beneath the moon; unsigned

IN79
Four-case Lacquer Inro

Unsigned
19th century

Inlaid with an overall arabesque *(karakusa)* design in fine gold wire on a tortoiseshell lacquer ground; the interior is of orange-gold *nashiji,* the shoulders and rims of *fundame.*

Ojime: abstract miniature designs in gold *hiramakie* on a brown ground
Netsuke: a *kagamibuta,* the bowl similar to the ojime, while the disc is of red lacquer with an eight-petal design outlined in tiny gold circles; unsigned

Provenance:
Bluette Kirchhoff collection

IN80
Four-case Lacquer Inro

Signed *Somada* (Family name) *saku*
19th century

Of hexagonal section, decorated with fourteen *iroe* dragonflies on an elaborate ground of various brocade designs (fifteen to each side) in *aogai, kirigane* and *kinji,* the exterior cord runners of *gyobu-nashiji,*; the interior is of thick *nashiji,* the rims of *fundame.*

Ojime: red coral bead
Netsuke: small lacquer table of Chinese form, of various lacquers, the top with a five-petalled design in aogai; unsigned

Provenance:
Roberta Pincus collection

IN81
Four-case *Tsuishu* Lacquer Inro

Signed *Zonsei* with *kakihan*
19th century

Carved on either side with a shaped panel, one with two sages playing *go*, the other with a seated scholar seated on a verandah and holding an *uchiwa* while looking out at two cranes in a garden, on a ground of carved clouds; the interior of matt black lacquer.

Ojime: *tsuishu* lacquer, two *shishi* in clouds on a diaper ground; signed *Tomone zu, Yosei to* (carved by Yosei, after a design by [Kobori] Tomone)

Netsuke: lacquered wood *hako* netsuke with design of sages in a garden; unsigned

IN82
Four-case *Tsuishu* Lacquer Inro

Signed inside *Fujiwara Chikanaga*
with *kakihan*
19th century

Deeply carved all over with a six-sided geometric design; the interior is of orange-red lacquer, the shoulders and rims of *fundame*.

Ojime: mottled glass bead
Netsuke: *tsuishu* lacquer, small
table on a base with a
carved design of a sage
and trees beside a
waterfall; unsigned

Provenance:
Edward H. Williams collection

IN83
Four-case *Tsuikoku* Lacquer Inro

Unsigned
19th century

Chinese style buildings and willow trees, with a bridge over a stream, carved in the Ryukyu manner on a ground of formalised waves and stars, the top carved with drapes and the bottom with an *uchiwa;* the interior is of matt black lacquer.

Ojime: carnelian bead
Netsuke: black lacquered wood *manju,* with tea ceremony utensils inlaid in tinted ivory and shell on a star diaper ground; unsigned

IN84
Miniature Three-case Lacquer Inro

Unsigned
19th century

A large lotus bloom inlaid in *raden,* with leaves in simulated pewter and brown lacquer with thin gold lacquer stems and flecks of *aogai,* the reverse with a single lotus bud in *raden;* the interior is of black lacquer, the bottom case lined with silver.

Ojime: silver with a design of two flying herons
Netsuke: wood, snail on mushroom; unsigned

Published:
Japanese Lacquer From Southern California Collections, p. 22

Exhibited:
Pasadena, California, 1991

IN85
Miniature Single-case Lacquer Inro

Unsigned, Rimpa style
19th century

An open fan, decorated with pine branches and flowering plum, inlaid in *aogai, raden* and pewter, the reverse with three upright plum branches, on a ground of *kinji,* sprinkled with gold flakes; the interior is of *nashiji,* the rims and shoulders of *fundame.*

Ojime: coral bead
Netsuke: miniature lacquer *hako,* with grasses in *hiramakie* on a kinji and gold speckled ground; unsigned

The design on both sides is very much in the Rimpa tradition, and is possibly after an original design by Ogata Korin (1658–1716).

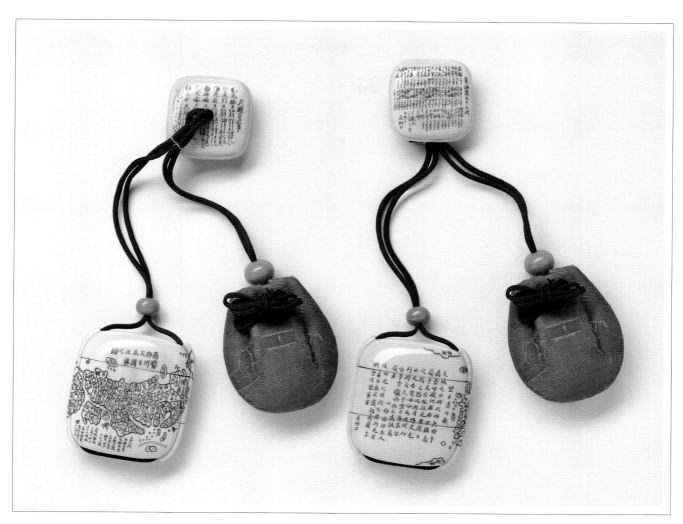

IN86
Two-case Ivory Inro

Signed *Nanka* (Ichimuken Nanka, Izumo province)
Early 19th century

Engraved with a map of Japan, showing the sixty-nine provinces and with a long inscription beneath, the reverse engraved with poems in the Chinese manner, by Yamabe-no-Akahito, all executed in delicate *kebori*.

Ojime: red coral bead

Netsuke: ivory, two-part *manju,* engraved on one side with the distances between towns on the Tokaido Road, and on the other with the days of good and bad luck in the Oriental calendar; signed *Nanka to*

Provenance:

Michael Tomkinson collection (the inro)
H.G. Beasley collection (netsuke and ojime)

Published:

Anne Hull Grundy, *Netsuke by Nanka and Nanyo,* in the magazine *Oriental Art,* Vol. III, no. 3, 1961
H.L. Joly and K. Tomita, *Japanese Art and Handicraft,* 132, illustrated, pl. XCVII

Exhibited:

London, 1915

IN87
Three-case Ivory Inro

Unsigned
Osaka, early 19th century

Chrysanthemums and other flowers carved in high relief on either side, on a finely incised ground, the cord runners carved with *karakusa;* the interior is of gold lacquer.

Ojime: ivory bead

Netsuke: ivory *manju,* carved with a branch of flowering magnolia against the moon on an *ishime* ground; unsigned, style of Tokoku

IN88
Three-case Wood Inro

Signed *Reikaku*
19th century

In the form of the bell of Dojoji, the handle in the form of two dragons *affrontés* holding a mother-of-pearl ball within their joined mouths, the sides carved with panels of *tennin* holding a *sho* and lotus bud amid a constellation and clouds.

Ojime: wood, flattened bead with landscape design

Netsuke: wood, two-part *manju* carved *á jour* with a dragon coiled around the top and sides, its eyes of *raden;* unsigned

IN89
Four-case Wood Inro

Signed on an inlaid mother-of-pearl cartouche *Kisui, Mimasaka*
19th century

Carved with an overall design of elongated delicate hydra dragons in relief.

Ojime: small metal disc, inlaid with three geese of gold and silver

Netsuke: dark wood, chrysanthemum *(kiku)* bloom and foliage with folded papers floating on water; signed *Toshinaga*

The signature on the inro indicates that it was made by Kisui (of) Mimasaka (province).

IN90
Three-case Wood Inro

Signed with a *kakihan*
19th century

Carved in the form of a turtle, its limbs retracted for compactness, the curled feet forming the cord attachment and the eyes inlaid; the interior is of dark brown lacquer with yellow lacquered risers.

Ojime: wood bead, carved with the *Sembazuru* (Thousand Crane) design; signed *Seimin*

Netsuke: wood, *awabi;* signed with *ukibori* characters *Bokuzan*

IN91
Two-case Cherry-bark Inro

Unsigned
19th century

A courtier's elaborate head gear resting among falling cherry petals, variously inlaid in tortoiseshell, *raden,* gilt metal, silver and green quartz, the cord runners of silver, unusually modelled as cherry blossoms and cherry buds with leaves.

Ojime: green glass bead
Netsuke: bamboo *hako,* the upper surface of cherry bark, with a running horse and grasses in gold and brown lacquer; signed *Koma saku*

IN92
Four-case Woven Rattan Saya Inro

Unsigned
19th century

The tightly woven inro *(otoshi)* enclosed in a sheath *(saya)* with a woven formal openwork design.

Ojime: small woven rattan, *en suite* with the inro
Netsuke: woven rattan ashtray netsuke, with metal lining; unsigned

Published:
NK, vol. 7, no. 2, p. 22, fig. 9

IN93
Miniature Single-case Silver Inro

Unsigned
19th century

Cast on both sides with an identical design of a large chrysanthemum *(kiku)* bloom with two buds and leaves, four large silver loops for the cord runners.

Ojime: silver openwork moon
Netsuke: none

IN94
Miniature Single-case *Shakudo* Inro

Signed *Ikki* with inlaid seal *Ko*
19th century

Engraved with autumn grasses beside a stream, partly inlaid in gold and silver *nunome*; the interior of silver.

Ojime: dark blue glass bead
Netsuke: *kagamibuta,* the polished dark wood bowl bearing a dark *shibuichi* disc with a similar design to the inro; unsigned

IN95
Three-case Lacquer Saya Inro

Signed *Nemoto saku*
Late 19th century

The sheath *(saya)* of uchiwa form, decorated in Shibayama style with exotic scenes of long-nosed *tengu* fishing, an elephant tossing fish to children, three blind men crossing a stream on a large millipede and a whale swallowing or disgorging a man, all among flowering trees, the inlay of mother-of-pearl, various hardstones, metal, horn, tortoiseshell, coral and painted ivory, the landscape background of gold *takamakie* with a profusion of *kirigane* and *e-nashiji;* the *otoshi* (inro) bears various brocade designs in delicate *togidashi-e* and e-nashiji, the interior is of red-gold *nashiji,* the shoulders and rims of *fundame.*

Ojime: pearl bead
Netsuke: *kagamibuta,* the ivory bowl with hammered bronze disc, inlaid with sea shells and weed in various materials; signed *Shibayama*

IN96
Five-case Lacquer Inro

Signed *Shunsui*
Meiji/Taisho period (1868–1926)

Scattered pheasant feathers in gold, silver and orange-red *togidashi-e* on a rich *roiro* ground; the interior is of rich red-gold *nashiji*.

Ojime: coral bead
Netsuke: two-part black lacquered *manju,* with oak leaves in gold *hiramakie,* the reverse with *sosho* calligraphy, signed *Jokasai*

Published:
Japanese Lacquer from Southern California Collections, 1991, p. 23
NK, vol. 7, no. 2, p. 21, no. 3

Exhibited:
Pasadena, California, 1991

IN97
Two-case Lacquer Inro

Signed *Oyama tsukuru*
20th century

A large persimmon and two chestnuts in gold, orange-red, brown, green and white *takamakie,* the reverse with two mushrooms on a fern leaf in similar style, all on a dark green ground; the interior of *nashiji,* the rims of *fundame.*

Ojime: lacquered mushroom by Sadae Walters
Netsuke: heavily stained and lacquered ivory, roasted chestnut, burst open to show the white meat inside; signed *Ryokuzan*

Provenance:
Hans and Margaret Conried collection

Published:
Alain Ducros, *Netsuke et Sagemono,* 1987, no. 245

IN98
Two-case Porcelain Inro

By *Armin Muller*
Santa Barbara, California, 1994

Of cylindrical form, covered with a pale celadon glaze, with ojime and netsuke *en suite,* all with a bamboo theme, the inro shaped as a broken section of bamboo, with leaves and three ants in relief.

Ojime: porcelain, small frog on a bamboo node
Netsuke: porcelain, bamboo tea whisk *(chasen)*

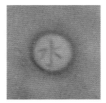

IN99
Three-case Porcelain Inro

By *Armin Muller*
Santa Barbara, California, 1991

The inro, with ojime and netsuke *en suite,* illustrates the famous poem by Basho,

> *"Old pond,*
> *frog leaps in.*
> *Splash"*

Of cylindrical form, covered with a pale celadon glaze, the inro with lotus in a pond, with irises on the reverse, on one leaf of which is perched a dragonfly.

Ojime: porcelain, cylindrical bead, a flying dragonfly on either side
Netsuke: porcelain, a frog resting on a large lotus pad

The pipe-cases are categorised by type, as follows:

Muso-zutsu: formed of two parts, one slightly smaller than the other, fitting into the saya (lower part) at the top, forming a stopper.

Aikuchi-zutsu: similar to *muso-zutsu*, the top of similar diameter to the *saya*.

Otoshi-zutsu: formed of a single decorated piece of material, in which the pipe fits, bowl downwards. This type is generally, but not always, made of stag-antler.

Wari-zutsu: of similar basic shape to the *otoshi-zutsu*, but having lateral splits to allow for the pipe to be slotted in.

Senryu-zutsu: made of a single section of material, the pipe locating in a shaped hole at the base while the mouth piece is held by a ring at the top which forms part of the decoration.

The size of *kiseruzutsu* show little variation. The average length is between 7¾ and 9⅜in (19.5 to 24cm). Where there is a large difference, it is mentioned in the catalogue entry.

Sagemono

KISERUZUTSU (PIPE-CASES)

S1
Stag-antler

Unsigned
mid to late 19th century

Kannon riding on a giant carp amid turbulent waves, part of which form the cord attachment, all carved in high relief.

Provenance:
Raymond and Frances Bushell collection

S3
Stag-antler

Signed *Bairyu sanjin Tokoku* with gold seal *Bairyu*
Cyclically dated *Tsuchino-to chuaki* (mid autumn, 1879)

A crab scurrying beside a rock among waving fronds of wild orchid, carved in low and high relief.

Provenance:
Irving Gould collection

Published:
Kurstin and Ortega, Masterworks of Netsuke, p. 87, no. 122b
NK, vol. 4, no. 1, p. 33, figs. 1, 1a and 1b

S2
Stag-antler

Signed *Ikkosai Somin* with *kakihan*
19th century

The Chinese poet Shaen seated in a grotto and reading by the light of a bagful of fireflies, all in delicate low relief, the rim carved with a band of *karakusa* with a *tomoe-mon* and the cord attachment formed as a *reishi* sceptre.

Published:
Kurstin and Ortega, *Masterworks of Netsuke*, p. 88, no. 123a

Shaen was a Chinese sage who was too poor to purchase illuminating materials so he gathered glow-worms in gauze bags and studied by the light they emitted.

S4
Stained stag-antler

Unsigned
19th century

Curled lotus leaves beneath the crescent moon, inlaid in gold and silver metal.

S5
Stag-antler

Signed *Bairitsuen Tokoku* with seal
Late 19th century

Engraved with a Chinese sage, probably intended for Toyu, holding an *uchiwa,* his head upturned as he watches a crane fly above, all carved in *katakiri* and *kebori* with fluid and crisp flowing lines.

Provenance:
William and Betty Parker collection

Published:
Kurstin and Ortega, *Masterworks of Netsuke,* p. 87, no. 122a

S6
Stag-antler

Signed in seal form *Kyo*
Late 19th century

Carved to simulate a section of bamboo, the rim and cord attachment of gold.

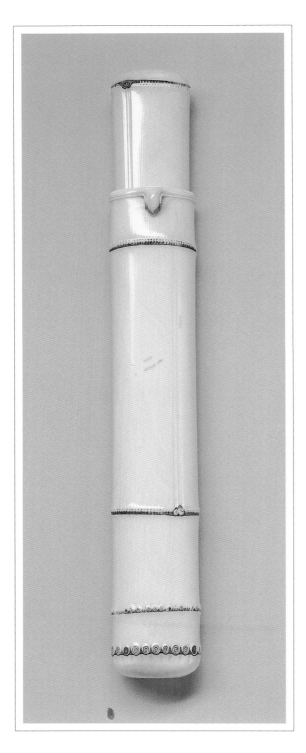

S8
Ivory

Signed *Shiryu (Yukitaka)* with seal
(unread)
19th century

Carved all over in *shishiaibori* with a mass of
flowering plants, details in *katakiri,* the cord
attachment in the form of a climbing frog.

S7
Ivory

Signed in seal form *Shiko*
Late 19th century

Carved to simulate a section
of bamboo.

S9
Ivory

Unsigned
19th century

Carved all over with a mass of flowering plants, with inlays of *aogai, raden* and various hardstones.

Published:
Kurstin and Ortega, *Masterworks of Netsuke,* p. 87, no. 122c

S10
Ivory

Unsigned
19th century

An overall design of meticulously engraved formalised waves with black staining.

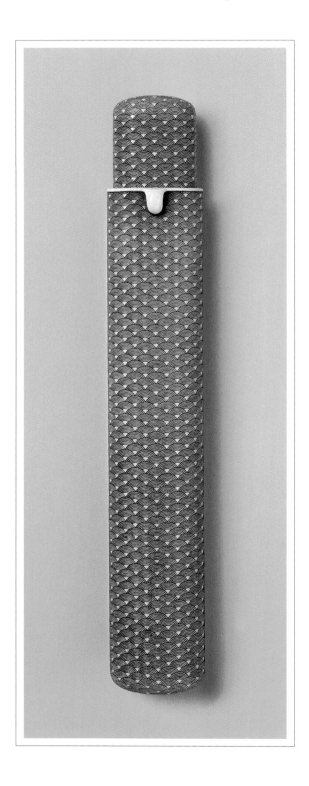

S11
Ivory

Signed Homin
19th century

Elegant design of chrysanthemums (kiku), plum blossoms (ume), orchids (ran) and bamboo (take) leaves carved in shishiaibori amid clouds on a black stained ground, a branch of plum blossom forming the cord attachment.

The plants depicted here are known as the four noble plants (*shikunshi*).

Published:
Kurstin and Ortega, *Masterworks of Netsuke,* p. 88, no. 123c

S12
Ivory

Signed *Homin*
19th century

Carved in relief with a stylised figure wearing a plumed hat and holding a lotus plant, within an elaborately shaped cartouche, below a fierce toothy mask whose nostrils form the cord attachment, the top and bottom are carved with gadroons and the reverse bears the engraved inscription, probably by a previous owner, *Meiji mizunoe uma ju rasu, Tokyo maru chu, Uramatsu sanjin to* (Carved on October 19th, in the 19th year of Meiji (1886), in Tokyo, by old man Uramatsu).

The design shows affinities with those taken from Spanish leather designs, illustrated in *Soken Kisho,* by Inaba Tsuryu, Osaka, 1781.

S13
Ivory

Signed *Naniwa Akiyuki*
Osaka, 19th century

Engraved all over with running calligraphy above a traveller's hat and staff, representing the poet Saigyo Hoshi.

The poet Saigyo Hoshi is often shown resting on the lower slopes of Fujiyama and gazing up to the peak while he composes a poem in his head. The subject is often alluded to by his hat and staff as shown here.

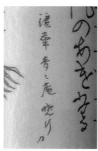

S14
Ivory

Signed *Bokkoku* for the ivory and *Rosetsu* for the inlay
19th century

Inlaid in *aogai* with five swimming and leaping carp in delicately carved swirling water.

Provenance
Raymond and Frances Bushell collection

Published:
INSJ, vol. 22, no. 4, p.28, figs. 12 a and 12b

S15
Walrus Tusk

Signed *Nobuyuki*
19th century

Carved in relief with Rosei's dream, the man recumbent upon a bench, while above is shown his dream of greatness in the form of a procession among swirling clouds.

S17
Lacquered Wood

Unsigned
Late 19th century

The pale burlwood covered with clear lacquer and lacquered with swarms of fireflies in black *takamakie,* each with a spot of red lacquer, over gold lacquered grasses, beneath an angled bridge, the rim and cord attachment of gilt metal.

S16
Lacquered *kaki*-wood

Signed on an inlaid gold tablet
Kaiseki
19th century

A magnolia branch of black lacquer, with gold buds and stamens, part of the branch forming the cord attachment, all on a black lacquered ground with *ishime* surface.

S18
Lacquer

Unsigned
19th century

A dragon among swirling clouds, in gold and red *togidashi-e* with details of *e-nashiji,* on a *roiro* ground with sprinkled gold powder.

S20
Lacquer

Signed *Moei (Shigenaga)*
19th century

A peacock among peonies and foliage, in gold, red and *shibuichi takamakie,* on a *roiro* and *muranashiji* ground with details of *kirigane.*

S19
Lacquer

Signed *Taisai* and *Tosen*
Late 19th century

An intricate design of spring flowers and grasses, in gold, silver, black and red *takamakie* with details of *aogai,* on a matt brown ground, the rim and cord attachment of gold.

S21
Lacquer

Signed *Keishin*
Late 19th century

Momotaro, the "Little Peachling," with his companions, a monkey, boar and pheasant, all depicted in gold, silver, brown and red *togidashi-e* on a *roiro* ground, the rim and cord attachment of gold.

Momotaro is the subject of a fairy-tale which relates the story of a poor woodcutter and his wife who fished a large peach from a river which, when the man cut it open, revealed a boy, whom they adopted as a gift from the gods.

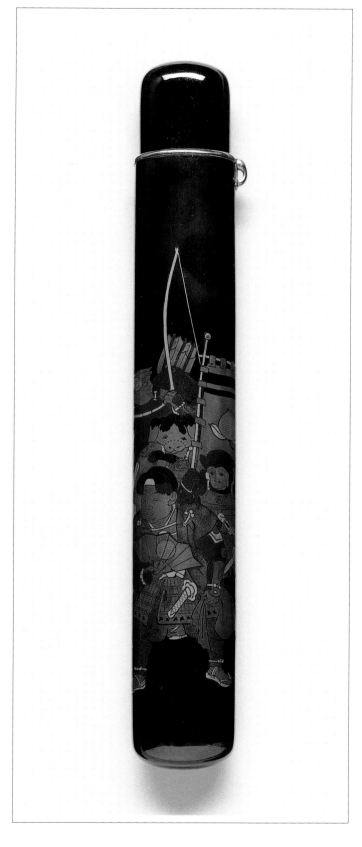

S22
Lacquer

Signed *Hashi-ichi*
19th century

Cleverly designed to simulate a two-node
section of bamboo, lacquered reddish-
brown with small black spots, the rim
and cord attachment of iron.

S23
Lacquer

Signed *Hashi-ichi*
19th century

Designed to simulate a section of bamboo in reddish-brown lacquer with black spots, inlaid in silver with Jurojin standing, holding an *uchiwa*, the rim and cord attachment of stag-antler with carved designs.

Published:
NK, vol. 11, no. 2, pp. 18, 19, figs. 12a and 12b

S24
Wood and lacquer

Signed, in seal form, *Bokkoku*
19th century

The boxwood *saya* lacquered on one side with a maple tree, in green-black *ishime*, with a scattering of autumn leaves in a variety of gold, black and red *takamakie*, in the manner of Rimpa school painting, the reverse is similarly lacquered with a branch and the top bears scattered leaves, inscribed Hoitsu *no zu* (after the painting by Hoitsu (Sakai Hoitsu, 1761-1828)).

Published:
INSJ, vol. 22, no. 4, p. 34, pl. 17a–b

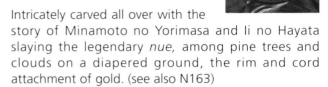

S26
Tsuishu lacquer

Signed *Hokei*
19th century

Intricately carved all over with the story of Minamoto no Yorimasa and Ii no Hayata slaying the legendary *nue,* among pine trees and clouds on a diapered ground, the rim and cord attachment of gold. (see also N163)

S25
Tsuishu lacquer

Signed *Baiun*
19th century

Carved with an overall Chinese-style landscape, with temples and a horse-retreat among pine trees and foliage on a steep mountainside, a waterfall cascading among the hills, carved through the lacquer and shown as a stylised wave ground in brown lacquer.

S27
Lacquer

Unsigned
19th century

Covered all over with a *tsugaru-nuri* design in black on an orange-red ground, liberally sprinkled with *aogai* powder, the rim and cord attachment of silver.

S28
Lacquer

Unsigned
19th century

Cut sections of seed pods inlaid with seeds of *aogai*, on a dark ground, filled with fine strands of hemp *(shuroke-nuri)* and sprinkled *aogai* powder.

S29
Lacquer

Unsigned
19th century

Entirely lacquered in *byakudan-nuri,* of gold and black lacquer rubbed down over a black ground.

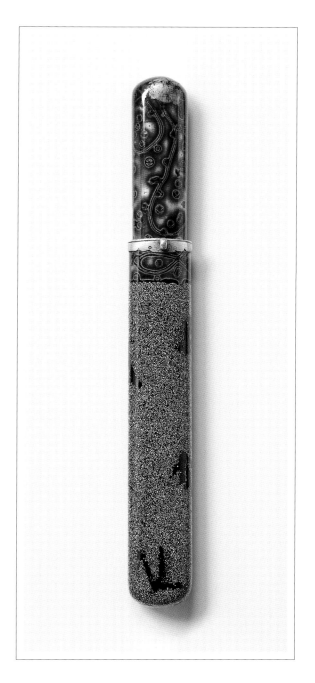

S30
Lacquer and crushed eggshell

Unsigned
Late 19th century

The upper part of *wakasa-nuri,* while the *saya* is covered with finely crushed eggshell on a black lacquer ground and lacquered with abstract shapes, the rim and cord attachment of silver.

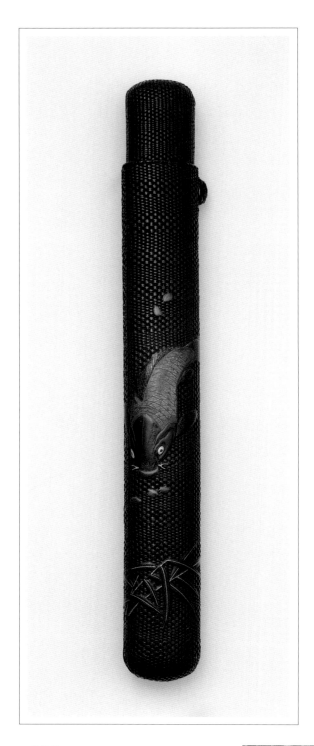

S32
Woven Reed

Signed, in a mother-of-pearl cartouche *Shogyoku*
19th century

The Chinese philosopher Moshi (Ch: Meng-tsu) and his mother, inlaid in wood and ivory, the rim and cord attachment of gold.

Moshi was a celebrated Chinese philosopher who, as a boy, was disagreeable and disobedient one day. To reprimand him, his mother slashed a beautiful piece of material that she had been weaving, causing him to repent and, subsequently, to become a responsible adult.

S31
Twisted Paper and Lacquer

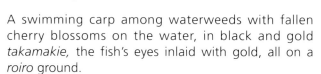

Signed *Kosai*
19th century

A swimming carp among waterweeds with fallen cherry blossoms on the water, in black and gold *takamakie,* the fish's eyes inlaid with gold, all on a *roiro* ground.

S33
Woven Bamboo

Unsigned
Late 19th century

The black and brown bamboo strips
lacquered all over, with a large bee
alighting on a chrysanthemum *(kiku)*
bloom and foliage in gold and brown
takamakie, sprinkled with gold powder.

S34
Tortoiseshell

Unsigned
Late 19th century

Formed of woven strips of black and tan tortoiseshell in a diagonal pattern.

S35
Plaited red Sandalwood (*shitan*)

Signed *Shokyo*
19th century

A broken roof tile in black *takamakie*, its end bearing an *aoi-mon* in *aogai*, among a spray of pinks (*nadeshiko*), their blossoms and buds inlaid with *raden*, its leaves of green-stained ivory, gold and black lacquer, the rim and cord attachment of gold.

S36
Bamboo

Signed *Tessai* (Kano Tessai)
Late 19th century

Finely engraved with sixteen scholars, poets and musicians with their attendants, a *shishi* and dragon at the lower edge and a long inscription on the reverse.

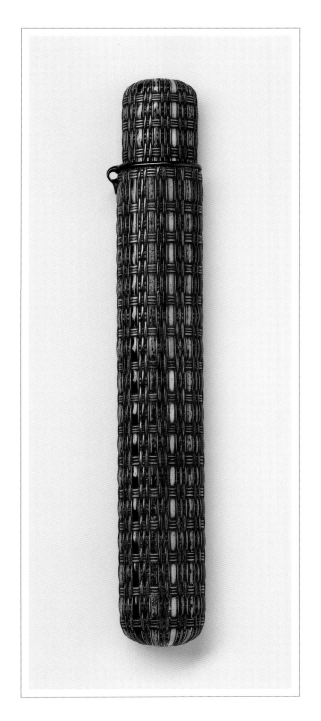

S37
Various Materials

Signed on a lacquered metal tablet *Seiko*
19th century

Interwoven strips of various species of bamboo with strips of stag-antler and tortoiseshell, the rim and cord attachment of metal.

S38
Stag-antler and Beaten Pewter

Unsigned
19th century

The base of stag-antler, carved in relief with a *ho-o* bird at the top and a dragon below, among clouds and *karakusa*, entirely covered with beaten pewter, except for the dragon and the body and head of the ho-o, which remain in stag-antler.

On one of the bird's long tail feathers is engraved the name Annie Hays Byers, presumably that of a previous owner.

S40
Lacquer

Unsigned
19th century

Flowers, butterflies and arabesques in swirling red and black lacquer, a lacquered butterfly forming the cord attachment.

S39
Carved Lacquer, 10 3/4in

Signed *Bunkido zo*
19th century

Flowering lotus plants, butterflies and dragonflies deeply carved in *tsuikoku* lacquer on a *tsuishu* ground, the top densely carved with formalised flowers, with *rinzu* rims.

S41
Stag-antler

Unsigned
19th century

Carved with a braided pattern on the face, simulating basketwork.

S42
Stag-antler

Unsigned, Asakusa style
Late 19th century

A long-nosed water dragon amid swirling waves, carved in relief, the dragon's eyes inlaid.

Published:
Kurstin and Ortega, *Masterworks of Netsuke,* p.89, no. 124b

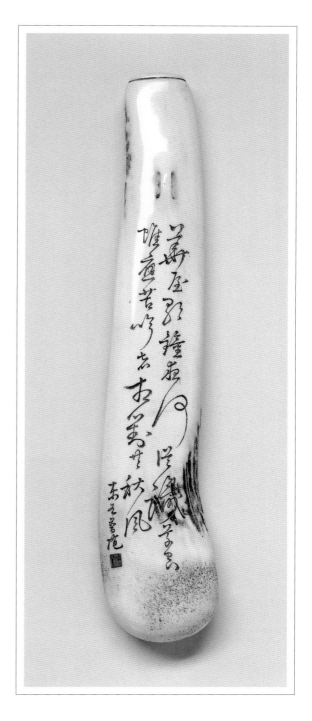

S43
Stag-antler

Signed *Tokoku Fuzui* with gold seal *Bairyu*
Tokyo, late 19th century

The natural stag-antler on the face is devoid of decoration, while the reverse bears a long inscription above the large signature.

S44
Boxwood

Signed *Harumitsu*
Ise, late 19th century

A *samurai* and two retainers in a
mountain forest, one of the retainers
having loosed an arrow, missing its mark,
to the horror of the other two.

Provenance:
Col. J. Bellhouse Gaskell collection

S45
Otoshi-zutsu Variant

Wood, 10 1/2in.
Signed Ikko with seal *Hasegawa*
Tsu, early to mid 19th century

The story of Choryo and Kosekiko deeply carved and inlaid with ivory, mother-of-pearl, malachite, horn and gold metal, a *shibuichi* and gold cover opening at the touch of a button at the top and a silver fluted cord attachment at the side.

With pipe, the black hardwood stem with iron and silver fittings, inlaid with a butterfly and blossom in silver.

The Chinese legendary figure, Hwang She Kung (Kosekiko) dropped a shoe while riding over a bridge and it was reluctantly picked out of the water below by the hero Chang Liang (Choryo).

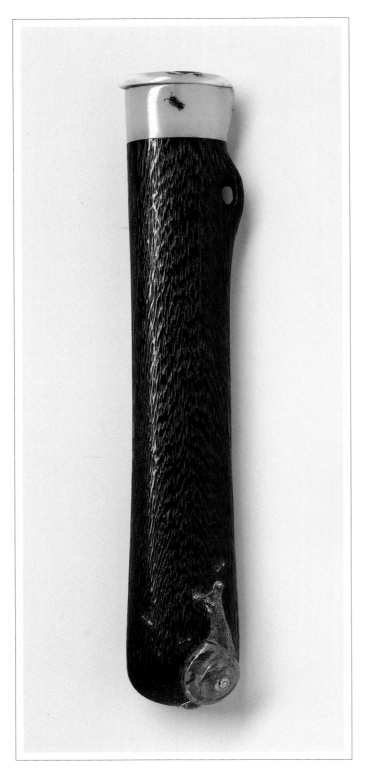

S46
Otoshi-zutsu Variant

Polished paulownia wood *(kiri-araidushi)*
Signed, on an inlaid metal tablet, *Jikan
Ganbun*
19th century

A snail, inlaid in pewter with natural snail
shell, and five large ants in gold, silver,
brass and *umimatsu,* the top fitted with a
horn sleeve and hinged stag-antler cover,
adorned with three further ants.

Published:
Kurstin and Ortega, *Masterworks of Netsuke,*
p.86, no.121b

S47
Stag-antler

Unsigned, Asakusa style
Late 19th century

Typically slit at the sides and carved in relief with a thin stylised *ho-o* bird and with three large *sosho* characters, *Kan zo gu*.

The inscription roughly translates, Examine this that I have made and proffer to you.

S48
Stag-antler

Unsigned
19th century

A *sake* vendor holding his bag of wares while drinking from a *tokkuri,* the spur of the antler effectively utilised to form the right arm and bottle, the eyes inlaid with dark horn pupils.

Published:
Kurstin and Ortega, *Masterworks of Netsuke,* p. 89, no. 124c

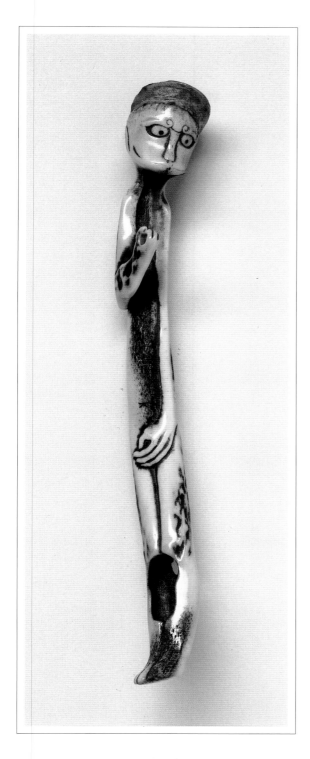

S49
Stag-antler

Unsigned
Late 19th century

In the form of a naked stylised *kappa*, one hand modestly covering his genitalia and his short left arm outstretched, his closed fist forming the cord attachment.

S50
Burlwood

Unsigned
Late 19th century

The lightly lacquered wood with a large black beetle among cherry blossoms and four fallen petals inlaid with silver, a large pewter pea pod to one side, its leaves lacquered in gold and green *takamakie* with *e-nashiji* details.

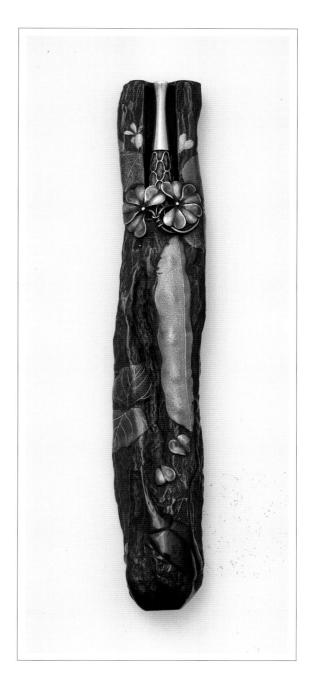

S52
Boxwood

Unsigned
19th century

Carved in the form of a long snake catching a frog in the coil of its tail, their eyes inlaid with brass.

S51
Ebony

Signed *Masateru* with *kakihan*
(Kaigyokudo Masateru)
Osaka, late 19th century

In the form of a *hossu,* a band holding the hairs together in red stained ivory and black lacquer, two tiny rosettes applied at the opening.

Published:
Kurstin and Ortega, *Masterworks of Netsuke,* p. 86, no. 121b

S53
Kiseruzutsu

Lacquered bamboo
Signed in seal form *Kan*

Of thin nodule section, *tan* lacquered and decorated with a large bean pod suspended from a leafy branch above a hovering dragonfly, all in brown and gold *takamakie* with details of *tsuishu* and *aogai*. A flattened section and the bottom bear formal floral designs in coloured lacquer on a black ground and, unusually, the case has a cover with an inset aogai disc carved with a dragon.

Kiseruzutsu with *Tabako-ire*

The pipe-cases that follow have been matched with *tabako-ire* (pouches for storing tobacco) by previous collectors. The pouches are generally rather simple, of leather or brocade and mounted with a clasp, generally in metal, formed of two parts. That on the face is called the *mae-kanagu* (or *kanamono),* and is simply for decoration, while that on the reverse, forming the actual clasp, is the *uraza.*

S54
Tomozutsu (matching set)

Kiseruzutsu of hide, very large and devoid of decoration

Tabako-ire of hide, with large metal *mae-kanagu* in the form of a running *shishi* with peony, the *uraza* of silver, both unsigned

Ojime: cloudy amber, deeply engraved with Shoki; signed *Mitsuhiro* with seal *Ohara*

Netsuke: ivory *manju,* engraved with a hawk perched among pine branches; unsigned

S55
Muzo-zutsu of Ivory

Signed *Tomoaki* with seal
Late 19th century

Plain, save for a carved pine branch which forms the cord attachment.

Tabako-ire of brown leather with ivory *mae-kanagu* carved as Kintoki and the giant carp, the *uraza* engraved with a willow and stream; both *mae-kanagu* and *uraza* signed *Mitsuhiro*.

Kintoki is another name for Kintaro (see IN62)

S56
Muso-zutsu of Ivory

Unsigned
Dated 1871

Carved in high relief with Josan no Miya playing with a white cat.

Tabako-ire of blue and gold brocade, the *mae-kanagu* in the form of the badger tea kettle *(bumbuku chagama)* in *shakudo* and bronze with gold details, the *uraza* of gold, signed *Tetsuga* (Tetsuo), *Meiji yo nen, matsu shoshun* (in the early spring of the fourth year of Meiji (1871)).

Published:
Kurstin and Ortega, *Masterworks of Netsuke,* p. 90, no. 125b

Josan no Miya was a beautiful attendant at the imperial court with whom Kashiwagi no Emon, a palace guard, fell in love. She is generally shown holding her pet cat on a silken leash.

The well-known story is derived from a Chinese Tang dynasty legend and was later adapted as a *No* play in Japan

S57
Muso-zutsu of Ivory

Signed *Bokko* with seal
19th century

Carved in finely detailed relief with Bunshosei, the Daoist star god of literature, shown as a running demon with long-clawed feet, holding a writing brush and a square measure *(tao),* his long hair streaming out and continuing on the reverse.

Tabako-ire of leather, the *mae-kanagu* of silver, carved with Saishi, one of the twenty-four paragons of filial piety, nursing her grandmother, while her baby looks on; unsigned.

Published:
INSJ, Vol. 22, no. 4, p. 30, Sigs. 15A (and on the cover)

S58
Otoshi-zutsu of Ivory

Signed *Shunkosai* with seal
Chogetsu
19th century

Tekkai *sennin* seated, blowing out
his soul, carved in high relief.

Tabako-ire of Dutch leather and
embroidered cloth, with a *shakudo* and gold
mae-kanagu in the form of a goose; unsigned.

The signature is illustrated in Lazarnick, *NIA,* p. 337.

S59
Muso-zutsu of Ivory

Signed on an inlaid gold tablet
Yuraku
19th century

Carved all over with flowering plum branches in relief,
the stamens inlaid with gold.

Tabako-ire of gold silk brocade, the *mae-kanagu* of
iron, in the form of a pine needle with a gold plum
blossom; signed *Norinaga,* the *uraza* of *shakudo,*
engraved with foliage.

S60
Muso-zutsu of Walrus tusk

Unsigned
19th century

Carved in relief with a flowering magnolia branch.

Tabako-ire of embroidered fabric with a design of
shishi and peonies, the silver *mae-kanagu* in the form
of a shishi, the *uraza* signed in seal form.

S61
Muso-zutsu of Lacquer

Signed *Taishin saku*
(Takagi Taishin) and
Moriyoshi
Late 19th century

A large inlaid silver heron standing among reeds at the
water's edge, in gold *hiramakie* on a *roiro* ground.

Tabako-ire of tan striped cloth, the *mae-kanagu* of
bronze in the form of a grasshopper on millet, signed
Moriyoshi; the *uraza* is of *shibuichi*, engraved with
rice stooks; signed *Yoshihiko*.

S62
Muso-zutsu of Lacquer

Signed *Taishin* (Ikeda Taishin)
Late 19th century

Various children's toys, in multi-coloured *takamakie* on a *tan* ground, with gold edged rim and cord attachment.

Tabako-ire of cloth with floral designs, the *mae-kanagu* of silver in the form of a plum blossom with bud, signed *Shunko;* the *uraza* of *shakudo,* engraved with pine needles; signed *Sadatoshi.*

Published:
Kurstin and Ortega, *Masterworks of Netsuke,* p. 90, no. 125a

S63
Muso-zutsu of Boxwood

Signed *Tessai* with *kakihan* (Kano Tessai)
Late 19th century

Okame seated, dressed in a richly patterned *kimono*, executed in *gesso*, beneath an inscription that translates: "Sculpture in wood of the dance pavilion of the Ebisu temple at Imaichi in the province of Yamato"; the reverse shows a large *oni* in dark green tinted gesso with an inscription, "Oni in ceramic at the feet of Shiteno in the Genko temple at Nara."

Tabako-ire of silk brocade, the mae-kanagu in the form of a spray of holly with a fish head, in shakudo and gold; signed Mitsuharu.

Provenance

Hans and Margaret Conried collection

Published:

NK, Vol. 8, no. 1, p. 45, figs. 5a and 5b

S64
Muso-zutsu of woven strands of Mulberry Tree

Signed with *tensho* characters
Doko
19th century

Inlaid with two puppies in ivory, one mottled brown, amid grasses in stained ivory, the rim and cord attachment of gold.

Tabako-ire of leather, the gold *mae-kanagu* in the form of a fish fin; unsigned.

S65
Muso-zutsu of Bamboo

Unsigned
Late 19th century

The flattened front polished and lacquered with three dragonflies in gold, silver red and black *takamakie*, over rice stalks engraved in *kebori*.

Tabako-ire of grey-green lambskin with an iron *mae-kanagu* in the form of a snail, the *uraza* of silver, engraved with bamboo in *hara-kiri;* both signed *Kitagawa* Hokusen of Mito.

Provenance:
William and Betty Parker collection

Published:
William and Betty Parker, The Japanese Personal Smoking Set, *Arts of Asia*, March/April 1983

S66
Tomozutsu (Matching set)

Unsigned
18th century

Kiseruzutsu of *senryu-zutsu* form, of *negoro*-lacquered wood, in the form of a dragon, and with brass eyes.

Tonkotsu carved and similarly lacquered with a dragon and clouds, with water droplets inlaid in brass.

Netsuke: in the form of a bowl held by three dragon claws; unsigned

The entire ensemble is symbolic of Handaka Sonja, one of the sixteen *Arhats* or *Rakan*, the disciples of Buddha. He is identified by the dragon, seen in a vaporous cloud issuing from his alms bowl.

S67
Tomozutsu

Unsigned
19th century

Natural wood, the *tonkotsu* of turned circular form, the kiseruzutsu of plain *muzo* form, with attached netsuke and ojime, all matching and devoid of decoration, the beauty purely in the grain of the wood.

S68
Tonkotsu

Unsigned
19th century

Natural *Reishi* Fungus, of tapering rectangular form, with wood cover and base.

Ojime: red glass bead
Netsuke: slab of natural *reishi* fungus; unsigned

The work was possibly by produced by *ainu*, the aboriginal race of Japan.

S69
Tonkotsu

Unsigned
19th century

Boxwood, of regular form, carved in relief with a dragon in fine detail, unsigned

S70
Tonkotsu

Inscribed in raised characters *Hekimen*
19th century

Polished Wood, in the form of Onna Daruma, the reverse carved with a *hossu*

Ojime: metal Daikoku
Netsuke: wood, mask of Okame; signed *Ikko*

S71
Tonkotsu with *Kiseruzutsu*

19th century

Polished Bamboo carved with four characters; signed *Shoko Heidai.*

Kiseruzutsu of natural bamboo, fitted with a slot at the top of the curved node, through which the pipe is slung and hangs free; unsigned.

S72
Tonkotsu with *Kiseruzutsu*

Signed on a boxwood cartouche *Onpo saku* with inlaid *kakihan*
19th century

Natural Wood, inlaid with a foliate branch in boxwood and mother-of-pearl, the cover surmounted by a green-stained ivory frog;

Kiseruzutsu of *otoshi-zutsu* form, of *kiriwood,* inlaid with a long snake winding around the shaft among rocks and grasses, inlaid with various woods, ivory and mother-of-pearl, an ivory slug forming the cord attachment; signed *Ikko.*

S73
Tonkotsu with *Kiseruzutsu*

Signed inside the cover *Ikkokusai*
19th century

Bamboo, of rough oval section, red lacquered with three crabs

Kiseruzutsu of senryu-*zutsu* form, of wood, lacquered with a snail and beetle in high relief; unsigned

S74
Tonkotsu

Signed on an inlaid pottery tablet *Teiji*
19th century

Polished Wood, of rectangular form with overlapping cover, lacquered with a grasshopper among vegetables, inlaid in variously glazed pottery;

Ojime: stag-antler fruit
Netsuke: ebony, two aubergines *(nasubi);* signed *Minko* with *kakihan*

S75
Tonkotsu

Unsigned

Thinly carved wood, of oval section with dark wood cover, lacquered in coloured *takamakie* with oak, maple and ginkgo leaves

Ojime: coral bead
Netsuke: stag-antler, standing deer; unsigned

S76
Tonkotsu

Unsigned
19th century

Wood, in the form of a frog, intricately carved to simulate the warty texture of the skin, the eyes of translucent horn with dark pupils.

Ojime: solid lacquer, carved in layers of different colours
Netsuke: wood, seated frog; signed *Shuji*

S77
Tonkotsu

The *uraza* signed *Mitsuhiro* with seal *Ohara*

Wood, shaped as a purse *(kinchaku)*, the clasp of ebony, in the form of a double gourd

Ojime: horn, in the form of a horse bit
Netsuke: copper, a stirrup *(abumi)*, with gilt metal floral medallions; unsigned

The horse bit, stirrup and gourd are all symbolic of the story of Chok'aro, who kept a magic miniature horse in a gourd.

Published:
NK, vol. 7, no. 2, p. 21, figs. 1a and 1b

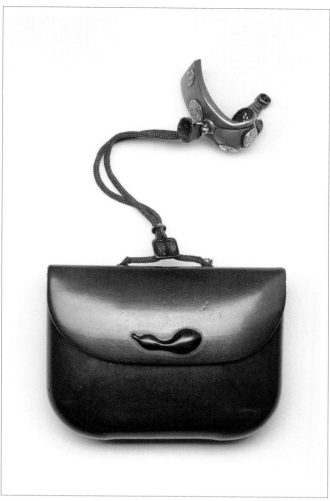

S78
Tonkotsu

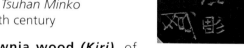

Signed *Tsuhan Minko*
late 18th century

Paulownia wood *(Kiri)*, of *bombé* form, inlaid with a woman holding a bamboo cane, a *torii* and stone lantern on the reverse, in ivory, pewter, wood, bone and horn. A natural shell rests on the cover, the underside of which bears a hidden compartment, opened by turning an ivory gourd-shaped knob

The subject is almost certainly that known as "The pilgrimage at the hour of the ox" *(ushi no toki mairi)*. This is a form of magic, generally practised by women, who nail to a tree in a temple grove an image of an enemy or inconstant lover, in order to facilitate their death.

S79
Tonkotsu

Signed *Minko, nana-ju-roku* (at the age of 76) with seal.

Wood, of *bombé* form, inlaid with a large aubergine *(nasubi)* and beans *(mame)* in *umimatsu* and coloured ivory, a green-stained ivory frog on the cover

Ojime: amber bead
Netsuke: two nasubi resting together, giving the appearance of a seated bird; signed *Kikuhiko*

From the statement of age, this *tonkotsu* could be dated to 1810

S80
Tonkotsu

Unsigned
19th century

Dark Polished *Reishi* fungus, lacquered to one side with a snail on stands of bamboo; unsigned.

Ojime: peach pit, carved with buildings
Netsuke: *reishi* fungus, applied with a snail in lacquered rhinoceros horn; unsigned

S81
Tonkotsu

Unsigned
19th century

Rootwood, inlaid with five metal ants in the manner of Jikan Ganbun.

Ojime: coral bead, lacquered with falling leaves

Kiseruzutsu of *senryu-zutsu* form, of natural wood, lacquered with a trailing vine and inscribed *Sei* (peaceful).

S82
Tonkotsu

Unsigned
19th century

Woven Reeds, twisted and lacquered in a lacy design over a wood base, the top and bottom with detailed spiderwork and braided patterns in woven reeds

Ojime: amber bead
Netsuke: ivory two-part *manju* carved with a filigree geometric pattern; unsigned

S83
Tonkotsu

Unsigned
19th century

Stag antler of square form, fashioned from three sections, each carefully plugged and devoid of decoration

Ojime: stag antler, four sided, carved with mythical bird and animal heads, their eyes inlaid, Asakusa school
Netsuke: stag antler, a seated laughing man holding his left foot; unsigned.

S84
Tonkotsu

Signed *Myochin saku*
19th century

Iron, in the form of the *bumbuku chagama,* (badger tea kettle) the badger's head to one side and a ladle *(hishaku)* attached to the cover

Ojime: stag antler, bat
Netsuke: wood, seated badger holding up its huge scrotum; signed
Toun gi saku (carved for fun)

S85
Kinchaku (purse)

Coconut shell and leather
Signed *Kiyo Masahide*
18th century

Carved in low relief with three water buffalo, one licking the back of her calf, their eyes inlaid in silver; the reverse is a leather purse with a small gold *mae-kanagu* in the form of a boar and dog.

Ojime: coral bead
Netsuke: wood, aubergine *(nasubi);* signed Minko

S86
Giotai

Unsigned
19th century

Of typical rectangular form, covered with ray-skin *(same)*, with a plain silver cover and applied on the face with a silver bar forming two flat arches, flanked by six silver fish in two rows. A leather thong encircles the container lengthwise to which is attached a single silver fish on the reverse.

Provenance:
Ann and Hy Meselson collection

The origins of the *Giotai* are rather obscure. The word first appeared in the Nara period (646–794) when it was used to describe a bag, called *Ittai*. We know it in its later form, as shown here, when it was apparently used to hold admission tickets for an audience with the emperor.

S87
Fude-zutsu (Brush-case)

Wood with inlay
Signed *Chohei sei*
Early 19th century

Of cylindrical form, inlaid with two long bean pods in green stained stag antler and black lacquer, with two large leaves in variously coloured *takamakie* and a bee in horn, metal, coral and gold lacquer, a slice of black lacquer incised in *chinkinbori* at the bottom edge.

Glossary

aogai Technique whereby tiny pieces of abalone *(awabi)* pearl-shell are inlaid into a lacquer ground. Similar to *raden* except that here the pieces of shell are much smaller, resulting in a much finer and more precise design.

aoi Hollyhock

asa-no-ha Geometric pattern of repeating star-like shapes that represent stylised hemp leaves.

Ashinaga and Tenaga Ashinaga ("long legs") and Tenaga ("long arm") represent a foreign race of people. They are typically shown fishing with Tenaga sitting upon the shoulders of Ashinaga and reaching down to grab a fish or octopus.

awabi Abalone shell with an iridescent mother-of-pearl lining that is used for inlays.

bakemono Any number of imaginary monsters or goblins, many appearing semi-human in form.

baku Beast of Chinese origin, made up from the parts of various animals with a lion's body, elephant's trunk, ox's ears and tiger's feet. *Baku* are believed to protect against bad dreams, which they purport to feed upon.

Baramon Mask used in *Gigaku* performances to represent Brahmin, the highest caste in the Indian social structure. Gigaku masks are more realistic than those used in other Japanese theatre, portraying a number of different racial types.

Benkei One of a number of legendary Japanese strong-men, this warrior-monk was, as a youth, known as Oniwaka (young devil). Benkei appears in Japanese theatre and is a popular subject in art where he is depicted in numerous ways based on the various legends about him.

Bishamon One of the Seven Gods of Good Fortune, this armour clad god of prosperity and strength is also one of the Guardian Deities of the Four Directions. In Japanese art, sculptures portraying Bishamon invariably show him with a trident in one hand and a small *pagoda* in the other, and often with a vanquished demon underfoot.

Bizen One of the six old kilns of Japan. Bizen pots are unglazed stonewares the colour—typically a reddish-brown—and surface decoration of which are achieved primarily through the accumulation of wood ash and the effects of firing. Early wares were principally jars and vessels for storage and household use. Later, production increased to include utensils for tea ceremony, flower vessels, bottles and statues.

bumbuku chagama This is the most familiar tale of the badger's power of transformation and tells of a priest who, upon heating his kettle of water, is horrified to see it sprouting a badger's head and legs and scampering off. See also *tanuki*.

byakudan-nuri Technique whereby metal foil or powder is applied to a lacquer surface and covered with a transparent layer of lacquer.

chasen Tea whisk.

chawan Tea bowl.

chidori Any of a number of small shorebirds found in Japan; often also referred to as plovers.

chinkinbori Technique whereby the design is incised into the lacquer surface and then filled with gold.

Chok'aro This Chinese Taoist immortal is said to have possessed a horse that he kept in a gourd. This magical creature had the ability to travel great distances without tiring and would take Chok'aro on long journeys.

Choryo Celebrated Chinese general most often shown in Japanese art in reference to his encounter with Kosekiko where he aids the old man and is rewarded with a scroll of military strategies that enable Choryo to become the most powerful in the land. Choryo and Kosekiko typically are shown on a bridge, Choryo with Kosekiko's shoe in his hand and the old man on horseback.

cloisonnè Enamel technique whereby a design is produced using extremely thin metal wires that are adhered to a metal form or base. These wires serve as partitions, creating enclosed areas that are filled with powdered coloured enamels. The object is fired, fusing the enamel and metal, and polished to a glass-like finish.

Daikoku One of the Seven Gods of Good Fortune, Daikoku is the god of wealth and prosperity. Like Hotei, he also carries a sack of treasures. He can be distinguished by his flat beret-like cap, small pointed beard and his magic mallet. In addition to his sack of treasures, he may be shown with bales of rice, symbols of a bountiful harvest, upon which are typically found his animal attributes, rats.

Daruma Indian priest who introduced Zen Buddhism to Japan. Numerous legends about Daruma exist, the most well-known being that of his nine-year long meditation during which his legs withered away. As a result, Daruma came to symbolise endurance. A popular theme in Japanese art, in particular netsuke, he is typically depicted in a humorous manner as a legless, round-bottomed and often armless figure alluding to the story above. This form also became a popular toy. Daruma is typically also shown holding a fly switch.

Dojoji, bell of Massive bell from the temple at Dojo. When appearing in art this bell typically refers to the legend of Kiyohime. See also Kiyohime.

ema A five-sided wooden tablet resembling a house in shape, which serves as an offering or token of gratitude to the gods. Offerings were originally horses but were later replaced by these votive tablets bearing a representation of the animal. Still later ema evolved to include a nearly unlimited range of imagery.

e-nashiji *Nashiji* technique used to create a design or picture rather than as a ground.

Fukai One of several similarly-styled masks used in *No* theatre to represent a distraught woman in mourning or facing tragic circumstances.

Fukurokuju One of the Seven Gods of Good Fortune, Fukurokuju symbolises happiness, wealth and long life. Like his counterparts, he has his own distinguishing characteristics: his bare elongated head, his long beard, and the fan that he carries.

fundame Technique whereby very fine gold powder is densely sprinkled onto a wet lacquer ground. The surface is left unpolished, resulting in a matt or dull finish.

Futen With his wind-filled sack, the god of wind, also known as Fujin, is typically depicted in Japanese art amid stormy skies. Like Raiden, the god of thunder, Futen is demon-like in appearance with horns and clawed-feet.

gaki Tormented spirit

Gama sennin One of many immortals, Gama sennin is accompanied by a magical three-legged toad. In Japanese art, he is one of the most frequently portrayed of the sennin, and appears often in netsuke form with the toad typically resting on his shoulder.

ginseng Family of plants, the roots of which were believed by the Chinese to have medicinal properties.

go Board game traditionally enjoyed by the Japanese aristocracy and considered one of the Four Gentlemanly Accomplishments. During the Edo period, it became a popular game played by all classes of Japanese society. Two players, using white and black markers on a grid-covered wooden board, attempt to capture the most territory.

go Art name

gofun White pigment made from pulverized oyster shells.

guri-bori: Carved lacquer technique whereby different coloured lacquers are applied in layers. After drying, the hardened surface is cut in v-shaped grooves, revealing the multiple layers. A distinctive scroll or spiral design is typically used in combination with this technique.

gyobu Referring to the individual application of large irregularly-shaped gold flakes.

gyobu-nashiji *Nashiji* technique using larger irregularly-shaped flakes that are carefully placed individually into the wet lacquer rather than sprinkled, creating a mosaic-like effect. Lacquer is applied to completely cover the flakes.

hagi Lespedeza or bush clover.

hakeme Technique whereby lacquer is applied with a stiff brush, leaving a design of visible brush strokes. It is derived from the Korean technique originally used to decorate pottery.

hako-netsuke Netsuke in the form of a lidded box.

Handaka Sonja Perhaps the most familiar of the sixteen *rakan* appearing in Japanese art, Handaka Sonja is typically shown holding an alms bowl from which issues a dragon.

Hannya Character appearing in *No* theatre that represents a woman whose feelings of jealousy and revenge have transformed her into a demon. The Hannya mask is probably the best known of the many masks used in No theatre. It portrays a wild woman with fang-like teeth and horns, and is used to portray Kiyohime in the play *Dojoji*.

harikata An artificial phallus.

himotoshi Openings on a netsuke through which the cord of the *inro* or other hanging container is threaded.

Hirado Porcelain ware named for Hirado Province (present day Nagasaki Prefecture) where it originated in the 17th century.

hiramakie Form of *makie* whereby the design is drawn in lacquer and sprinkled with powders. A thin protective layer of lacquer is applied and, when dry, the surface is polished to a flat finish.

hirame Technique typically used as a ground whereby flakes of gold are sprinkled onto a wet lacquer surface and later covered with clear lacquer and polished. The term *hirame* also refers to the tiny, irregularly-shaped, flattened flakes of gold metal themselves.

hirazogan Flat inlaid metal.

hogacho Subscription book or list of contributions.

ho-o Mythical bird similar to the phoenix and resembling a brightly coloured combination of peacock and pheasant with long tail feathers.

hossu Ritual fly switch made of animal hair and carried by Buddhist priests.

Hotei One of the Seven Gods of Good Fortune, this jolly god of contentment is probably the most well known and popular of this group. Hotei is characterised by his cheerful countenance, large belly and his sack of treasures, and is often depicted in the company of small children.

Ii no Hayata According to this legend, the palace was being besieged by the strange beast known as the *nue* whose nightly visits were causing the emperor ill health. After many nights of stalking the elusive creature, it was finally shot down by Minamoto no Yorimasa's arrow, the final death blow coming from the sword of his retainer, Ii no Hayata.

iroe Technique similar to togidashie except this variation includes the use of coloured powders.

ishime Technique used to produce a matt and rough-textured surface like that of stone.

Josan no Miya Considered witch-like creatures, cats have historically been unpopular in Japan. As such, they rarely appear in early Japanese art and when they do are frequently paired with Josan no Miya. Stories about this court lady and her association with cats vary though she is always easily distinguished by the presence of her pet with which she plays or holds by a leash.

Jurojin One of the Seven Gods of Good Fortune, Jurojin is the god of longevity and wisdom. He is distinguished by a somewhat elongated head that is covered by a headdress. His large head resembles that of Fukurokuju, a god also associated with longevity, with whom he is sometimes confused. He typically carries a staff or scroll and a fan and is usually accompanied by a deer, another symbol of longevity.

Kabuki Popular form of Japanese theatre that is very colourful and dynamic, consisting of acting, music and dance. Masks are not used in *Kabuki,* instead actors use heavy makeup to indicate their characters.

Kadori Myojin According to legend, this deity protects the world from earthquakes by using a magic gourd to subdue the earthquake fish and keep it from thrashing about. Though he rarely appears in Japanese art, he is often alluded to, particularly in netsuke, by the pairing of the catfish and gourd.

kagamibuta Type of netsuke consisting of a round shallow bowl, usually of ivory or wood, covered with a metal lid that is engraved, inlaid or otherwise decorated.

kaki Persimmon.

kakihan Personalised written seal used by an artist. Also called a *kao*, this monogram-like mark may be used alone or in addition to the artist's signature.

kana Japanese syllabic writing system consisting of phonetically read characters that represent sounds.

kanagai Sheets or strips of metal foil from which the geometric-shaped pieces used in *kirigane* are cut.

kanji Japanese system of writing based on Chinese characters.

Kannon Buddhist goddess of mercy who is represented in numerous forms. In one of her more familiar portrayals she is shown riding upon the back of a carp and as such she is known as Gyoran.

Kan'u Celebrated Chinese general and warrior god. Kan'u frequently appeared in Edo period Japanese art. He is easily distinguished by his elaborate Chinese-style robe tied with a long sash and the pose he invariably takes: his left hand stroking his famous long slender beard and in his right hand, his halberd.

kappa Imaginary amphibious creature that inhabits rivers or bodies of water and resembles a frog with a turtle carapace. Its monkey-like head has an indent on top filled with water, which is the source of its strength. This mischievous creature preys on the unwary, especially young women, and appears often in Japanese art.

karako Chinese children who frequently appear in netsuke in groups, playing with toys or instruments, or paired with Hotei. They are generally depicted as chubby and round-faced and can be distinguished by their foreign clothes and the two small tufts of hair on their otherwise bare heads.

karakusa Motif inspired by classical floral designs of Central Asia, consisting of flowing vines off which grow a variety of different leaves and flowers. This scrolling plant design is used to decorate the surface of an object, with little concern for the accuracy of the plants or flowers depicted.

Karasu tengu See *tengu*

katabori Carving in-the-round or figure-carving.

katakiri Technique in lacquer and metalwork where the surface is incised with cuts that imitate painted brush strokes.

kebori The engraving of fine lines of regular width and depth.

Kijo Mask similar to Hannya with a fierce grin and horns, though smaller in size. Like Hannya, this mask is used in *No* dramas to represent a demonic woman overcome with jealousy and rage.

kiku Chrysanthemum

Kikujido The Chrysanthemum Boy of Chinese legend who appears often in Japanese art and *No* plays. Kikujido wrote sacred Buddhist verses on the petals of chrysanthemum blossoms and set them adrift in a nearby stream. It is said that the waters in which these petals floated would impart wellness and everlasting youth. The pairing of a writing brush with chrysanthemums is an allusion to this legend.

kimono Traditional Japanese attire.

kimpun Very fine gold powder.

kinchaku Purse or money pouch worn suspended from the obi.

kinji Technique using gold powder densely sprinkled onto a wet lacquer ground and, when dry, polished to a high gloss finish.

Kintaro See Kintoki

Kintoki Legendary Japanese strong-man who as a youth was known as Kintaro ('golden boy'). He was raised by a mountain witch and had forest animals as companions, and is often shown in the company of animals, in particular a bear, and carrying an axe. A popular subject in Japanese theatre and art as both a youth and adult.

kiri Paulownia

kirigane Technique whereby metal foil, cut into small regularly-shaped pieces, is applied onto a lacquer ground. The foil is often cut into geometric shapes, such as squares or rectangles, and the finished surface resembles that of a mosaic.

kirimon Family crest of paulownia design.

kirin Mythical creature of Chinese origin composed of a number of different animals. It has a deer's body from which flames emit, horse's hooves, and a dragon's head with a single horn. Contrary to its frightful appearance, the kirin is an auspicious creature symbolising goodness and virtue and was a popular design motif.

kiseru Tobacco pipe

Kiyohime The legend of Kiyohime tells of her unrequited love for the priest Anchin. In her anger she traps him beneath the temple bell of Dojoji and then, after transforming into a serpent, sets the bell ablaze, killing them both. This story is often depicted in Japanese art and is the theme of several *No* and *Kabuki* plays.

Konoha tengu See *tengu*

Kosekiko Legendary Chinese sage, also called the Yellow Stone Elder. See also Choryo.

Kyogen Comic interludes that are performed between *No* plays. In contrast to No, few *Kyogen* roles incorporate the use of masks.

Magojiro Woman's mask, used in *No* theatre.

manju Form of netsuke named for the flat, round rice-cake that it resembles. *Manju* can be solid or two-part and though primarily circular can also be oval, rectangular or square in shape.

mokko Rounded square form with indented corners.

mokugyo Wooden temple gong used by Buddhist monks to accompany chanting.

mokume Surface simulating wood grain.

Momotaro One of the super-strong characters of Japanese legend, Momotaro is known as The Peach Boy. It is said that he was discovered in a peach by a woodcutter and his wife who adopted and raised him. As a powerful youth, he left one day to seek his fortune, accompanied by a dog, pheasant and monkey. He returned triumphant, bestowing upon the old couple riches and a life of prosperity.

Moso One of the Twenty-Four Paragons of Filial Piety. Moso's deed of devotion toward his mother is often symbolised in art by a bamboo shoot. His ailing mother longed for boiled bamboo shoots and, in the dead of winter, Moso, wearing a straw hat and with shovel in hand, searched the bamboo groves in hopes of fulfilling his mother's wish. To his amazement, his tears of desperation brought forth bamboo shoots from the frozen ground.

moxa Substance made from the fine hairs from the underside of mugwort leaves which is applied to the skin and ignited, and has been used in East Asia for centuries to relieve various ailments.

mura-nashiji *Nashiji* technique whereby the flakes are applied unevenly, in lighter and heavier quantities resulting in a cloud-like effect.

nashiji Technique typically used as a ground whereby irregularly shaped flakes of gold are sprinkled onto a wet lacquer surface and later covered with lacquer. After polishing, the final finish takes on an orange tone resembling the skin of a Japanese pear (*nashi*). It is also sometimes called aventurine, because of its resemblance to the type of speckled glass of that name.

negoro Technique whereby a ground of black lacquer is covered with a layer of red lacquer. The upper layer is polished down so that the black ground is visible in places creating a mottled effect reminiscent of a highly worn surface. The name derives from the Negoro temple near Mt. Koyasan, where Bishop Raiyu Sojo and his pupils made lacquer wares in this style in the 13th century.

No Classical Japanese theatre that combines acting with music and dance, and uses carved wood masks to identify characters. *No* themes are frequent subjects in Japanese art; the masks are a particular favourite of netsuke carvers.

nue Mythological creature composed of a monkey's head, badger's body, tiger's feet and a snake for a tail. See also Ii no Hayata.

nunome Lacquer technique used to simulate the texture of cloth.

O-Beshimi Type of mask used in *No* theatre. One of several demon-like characters with wide-open eyes, O-Beshimi can be distinguished by his tightly-closed mouth.

O-Tenjin *No* mask representing a powerful and angry Shinto god with glaring eyes under a furrowed brow, a moustache and an open mouth baring its teeth.

obi Sash or belt worn around the *kimono*.

Oharame Woman peddler from the village of Ohara. For centuries these women have sold their wares, namely flowers, vegetables and firewood, on the streets of Kyoto. Their distinctive attire consists of an indigo-coloured costume and a white head-covering, and they customarily carry their wares on their heads.

ohirame Large, thick, irregularly-shaped metallic flakes used as in a lacquered ground .

ojime Bead through which the cords of an *inro* are threaded and which slides down to keep the lid and sections of the inro tightly closed.

Okame Also known as Uzume or Otafuku, this legendary female deity personifies fun and merriment. She is the goddess of mirth, appearing in *Kyogen* performances. In Japanese art, depictions of her most often focus on her narrow forehead, rounded cheeks and button nose.

okibirame Technique whereby flat, irregularly-shaped metal flakes are set one-by-one into a wet lacquer ground without overlapping to form a distinct pattern.

Okina Term used to designate the *No* performance or the mask used in it. The Okina mask depicts a smiling elderly man with round bushy eyebrows and a long pointed beard and is used for the Okina, Senzai and Sanbaso dances. It is the only No mask that is constructed of two parts, the chin attached by cords to the upper part of the face.

oni Small demon with horns, claws and fang-like teeth. Though emblematic of evil, *oni* are generally perceived more as mischief-makers and bearers of ill fortune and in art are typically depicted in a humorous manner.

oni nembutsu Repentant demon who, having seemingly changed his ways, carries out the prescribed Buddhist rituals in hopes of gaining salvation.

Onna Daruma Depiction of Daruma as a woman.

otoshi Smaller, inner part of an *inro,* pipe-case or other type of two-piece container that fits within the outer sheath (*saya*).

raden Technique similar to *aogai,* except the pieces of shell used here are much larger, thicker and almost white. The term *raden* is sometimes erroneously used interchangeably with *aogai,* though their finished effects are quite different. In contrast to the very fine and delicate results obtained in aogai, in *raden* the effect is very bold.

Raiden God of Thunder and Lightning, this demon-like figure is also known as Raijin. In art, Raiden is sometimes treated in a humorous manner. He may be shown with thunderbolts. However his main attribute is his thunder drum decorated with a three-comma *(mitsu-tomoe)* design.

rakan Buddhist disciple. Though many in number, Japanese art generally focuses on a smaller group of sixteen who are portrayed with shaven heads, long earlobes often with earrings, and long eyebrows. They wear Buddhist cloaks, secured on one shoulder, leaving the other bare. In art, *rakan* often appear in groups and can be individually identified when accompanied by their specific attributes.

Rat's Wedding Japanese folktale that was a popular motif of *inro* makers. In art, this story is typically referenced by the depiction of a wedding procession of rats including rats carrying a palanquin.

reishi Magical fungus said to confer longevity and used as sceptres by Taoist immortals.

rinzu Key fret design , also known as a thunder pattern; derived from ancient Chinese pictographs representing thunder and used frequently as a border decoration.

rogin-nuri Silver-coloured lacquer ground, produced by mixing silver powder with the raw lacquer .

roiro Technique using multiple layers of black lacquer, each layer polished, resulting in a hard glossy wax-like finish.

Rosei Chinese figure best known for his famous dream. Discontented with his simple life, Rosei set out to seek his fortune. After much travelling he became weary and, laying his head upon a magic pillow, fell asleep. Accounts of his dream vary but all tell of fame and greatness tinged with tragedy. Rosei awakened, recognising his dream as a warning of the emptiness of a material life and contentedly returned home to his village. Depictions of a sleeping Rosei typically show him reclining on a bench and holding a fan while he sleeps.

Ryotohin One of the Chinese Eight Immortals of Taoism. A scholar and recluse who, with his magical sword, roamed the empire, slaying dragons and ridding the land of evil.

Ryujin The Dragon King of the Sea is a legendary character who controls the seas by the use of a tide-ruling gem. A popular netsuke subject generally depicted as a fierce bearded figure with a dragon atop his head and extending down his back. He is said to reside in a grand underwater palace and is often shown holding the tide-ruling jewel.

Ryusa Type of *manju* netsuke with pierced or openwork decoration named after the 18th century carver who developed the technique.

sabejinuri Lacquer ground simulating the appearance of old metal, in particular that of rusted iron.

Saigyo Hoshi Warrior who became a priest and poet, and spent much of his life travelling to pilgrimage centres and scenic spots throughout Japan. He is often portrayed in Japanese art in such a setting—often viewing Mt. Fuji—with a straw hat or walking stick in hand. Because Saigyo was an important poet depictions of him are sometimes accompanied by an inscription or poem.

sake Rice wine.

Sanbaso Ancient dance originally performed at religious ceremonies to appease the gods, and later performed in *Kabuki* theatre. *Sanbaso* is a vigorous dance, the dancer easily distinguished by the his Okina mask, tall striped hat and costume bearing pine and crane motifs.

Sambiki Saru Three Mystic Apes most familiar in the west as the monkeys who "see no evil, speak no evil, and hear no evil".

same See shagreen.

samurai Member of Japan's warrior class which was abolished in the mid-19th century.

Saru kani kassen The story of the feud between the monkey and the crab tells of a mean-spirited monkey who takes advantage of a crab. Later, the angry crab exacts revenge on the monkey. The pairing of a monkey and crab is an allusion to this tale.

Saruta hito This long-nosed mask represents the Shinto deity Saruta Hiko no Mikoto.

sashi Elongated form of netsuke that is inserted behind the *obi*.

saya Sheath or outer part of an *inro*, pipe-case or other type of two-piece container.

Seiobo Known as the Queen Mother of the West, Seiobo is one of the few female immortals. It is said that she had a garden in which peaches of immortality grew. She is one of the most frequently found *sennin* in Japanese art, typically shown with either a basket of peaches or a peach bough.

sennin Immortals of Chinese Taoist origin, usually depicted as mountain recluses wearing tattered garments and/or robes made of mugwort leaves. They appear frequently in Japanese art, typically in combination with the particular object or animal associated with them.

sentoku Gold coloured alloy of copper and other metals.

shagreen Fish, ray or shark skin.

shakudo Blue-black coloured alloy of copper with a small quantity of gold.

Shibaraku Famous *Kabuki* play, considered a classic example of the bold and exaggerated *aragoto* style of performance.

shibuichi Grey-colored alloy of copper and silver metals.

shibuichi-nuri Grey-colored lacquer ground, similar in appearance to the metal alloy *shibuichi*.

shishi *Kara-shishi* or Chinese lions are imaginary creatures of Chinese origin. They were very popular subjects in Japanese art, in particular as sculptures and netsuke. They are considered protectors from evil and, combined with peonies, symbolize imperial authority.

shishiaibori Type of sunken relief carving where the areas of relief remain below the level of the surrounding surface. This technique gives the illusion of great depth and was frequently used by carvers of *manju* netsuke.

shitan Red sandalwood or rosewood

sho Musical instrument, often referred to as a mouth organ, consisting of a bundle of thin reeds of various lengths atop a hollow round base fitted with a mouthpiece.

shogun The highest ranking military leader in pre-modern Japan.

shoji Large screens constructed of a wood frame covered with white paper that serve as sliding doors, window substitutes, or room dividers in traditional Japanese buildings.

shojo Imaginary elf-like beings from Chinese legend easily distinguished by their long red hair. These good-natured creatures are fond of *sake* and are often depicted in Japanese art paired with a *sake* cup or in the case of netsuke, in a drunken stupor. The *shojo* is also the subject of a *No* play.

Shoki Legendary figure of Chinese origin said to have been a scholar whose ghost protected the Tang dynasty emperor from demons. His role as a destroyer of evil spirits lead to his title "The Demon Queller". He appears in Japanese art as a fierce sword-wielding warrior, dressed in Chinese robes and wearing a scholar's cap. He has a full wide beard and is frequently shown in the company of a fleeing *oni*. He is often shown in netsuke in a humorous manner, with the much smaller oni seemingly outwitting the great hunter.

shunga Pictures of an erotic nature, and a popular subject in Edo period (1615-1868) *ukiyoe* prints.

sika Japanese deer said to live to a very old age and in art sometimes paired with other figures emblematic of longevity. The Kasuga shrine in Nara is famous for its tame deer and in art deer are frequently combined with a *torii* or cryptomeria trees in allusion to this celebrated site. Deer are emblems of autumn and, as such, are paired with the maple.

sosho Cursive style of writing described as 'grass script' due to its resemblance to flowing grasses. This abbreviated and artistic style is used primarily in calligraphy.

stupa Sacred *pagoda* or grave marker, often in the form of a multi-levelled pagoda.

sumie Painting executed in black ink (*sumi*).

tabako-ire Tobacco pouch worn suspended from the *obi*.

Tadamori and the Oil Thief One stormy night, Tadamori learned that a beast with flames coming from its mouth was lurking about the temple, and had been seen there for several nights past. He went in search of the monster, springing upon it only to discover that it was not a flame-eating monster at all, but merely a thief who had been stealing oil for his lamp. Allusions to this story show Tadamori apprehending the thief who wears a straw rain cape and hat, and holds a pot of oil in one hand.

Tagasode (Whose sleeves?) Painting theme popular during the early Edo period that depicts various garments hanging from a rack frequently surrounded by other personal effects and lacking a figural subject. The clothing and objects are intended to evoke the image of their owner—in this case, a beautiful woman. This theme is typically Japanese in its method of evoking the subject of the painting without portraying it outright.

takabori Relief carving technique.

takamakie Form of *makie* whereby parts of the design are built up by using multiple layers of lacquer sometimes combined with other materials such as clay or charcoal. The sprinkled decoration is applied when the desired surface height is achieved.

takaramono Treasures or precious objects representing good health, prosperity and happiness that are associated with the Seven Gods of Good Fortune.

takazogan High relief inlaid metal.

tan Red oxide of lead or cinnabar.

tanuki Resembling a Japanese badger or otherwise referred to as a "raccoon-dog", the *tanuki* is the source of much superstition and fear. In Japanese folklore it is known as a malevolent creature with supernatural powers and the ability to change form at will. See also *Bumbuku chagama*.

tatami Thick straw mats used as floor coverings in traditional Japanese homes.

Tekkai One of the Taoist immortals of Chinese origin. Tekkai had the ability to blow out his soul from his body, enabling it to travel great distances. On one occasion he released his spirit, leaving his body in the care of a disciple, but returned to find his body gone. With nowhere else for his soul to reside, he inhabited the first body he found available—that of a lame beggar. He is easily distinguished by his pose as he blows out his soul and by his tattered clothes and the iron crutch he uses.

tengu Mythical creature that inhabits forests and mountains, the *tengu* is a mischievous trouble-maker and possesses great physical strength. There are two kinds of tengu: *Konoha tengu* is of human form with a human face and greatly elongated nose; and *Karasu tengu* resembles a bird, with wings, a beak and clawed feet. *Karasu tengu* hatching from an egg *(tengu no tamago)* is a common subject in netsuke.

tennin Generally referred to as Buddhist angels, these celestial beings are Indian in origin. They can be distinguished by their flowing scarves or winged robes and the lotus blossom or musical instrument they carry. Because they are often depicted with nearly identical characteristics, the terms *tennin* and *karyobinga* are sometimes used interchangeably when describing these heavenly beings.

tensho Archaic seal-style characters.

Tobosaku This *sennin* gained his immortality via the magical peaches he stole from the garden of Seiobo. In depictions of him, Tobosaku is sometimes shown with a deer or, like the Queen Mother of the West, holding a peach. He can also be found paired with Seiobo.

togidashi-e Type of *makie* in which the final design or picture is completely flush with the ground. The picture is drawn with wet lacquer onto which powders are sprinkled and followed by successive layers of lacquer. When dry, the surface is repeatedly polished until the design reappears.

Tokaido The main highway between Edo (Tokyo) and Kyoto during the Edo period (1615-1868). Along the route were towns where travellers could rest and buy supplies. These fifty-three towns or stations gained fame as subjects in literature and art.

tokkuri Sake bottle.

tomoe-mon Family crest of double comma-like design.

torii Gateway at the entrance to a Shinto shrine.

Toyu Chinese sage who one day was visited by a pair of blue cranes, which he took as a sign that he was to join the immortals. He climbed upon the backs of the birds and was taken to Heaven. In depictions of Toyu he is thus shown riding upon the cranes or otherwise in combination with a crane.

tsuba Hand guard on a sword.

tsubo Storage jar or pot.

tsugaru-nuri Named after the province of Tsugaru where it is said to have originated, this technique involves several layers of different coloured lacquers which are applied unevenly to the base. When dry, they are polished flat, giving the surface a marbled appearance.

tsuikoku Technique originating in China of applying multiple layers of black lacquer into which the design or picture is carved.

tsuishu Technique originating in China of applying multiple layers of red lacquer into which the design or picture is carved.

uchikomi Pure gold nuggets that were inlaid into lacquer and used most often to represent rocks and knots on tree trunks.

uchiwa Rigid fan made of paper adhered to a thin bamboo frame with a handle. Uchiwa come in various shapes.

ukibori Carving technique used to achieve a relief effect. A design or picture is compressed into the surface of the wood. The surrounding raised surfaces are then brought down to the level of the compressed areas. The wood is soaked with water and the compressed areas expand, resulting in a raised design.

ukiyoe Literally "pictures of the floating world", *ukiyo-e* were images of contemporary society with subjects primarily derived from the *habitués* of the urban pleasure quarters such as courtesans and actors.

umebachi-mon Family crest of highly-stylised plum blossom design.

umimatsu Fossilized sea-pine.

Uzume See Okame.

wakasa-nuri Lacquer technique similar to *tsugaru-nuri* but with stronger yellows and browns. In addition, here foils or other objects such as leaves or pine needles are sometimes pressed into the wet lacquer leaving indentations when the surface is finally polished.

warabi Young fern.

yamimakie Form of *makie* whereby black or dark brown powders are sprinkled onto a dark lacquer ground.

Yorimasa Minamoto no Yorimasa was a famous poet and archer. The most famous tale of this great warrior recounts his slaying of the fierce creature, the *nue*. See also Ii no Hayata.

Yoshitsune Sembonzakura "Yoshitsune and the Thousand Cherry Trees" is one of the most popular plays in the *Kabuki* repertoire. Act V, "The Sushi Shop", is a frequently performed act from this play.

Subject Index

Index of Netsuke artists

Baitetsu 19th century. No details known.
N218

Birch, Michael Henry Born 1926 in Alexandria Egypt. Now lives in Tunbridge Wells, England. Michael Birch is a writer, poet, artist and has created a large number of netsuke, using a variety of materials, his inspiration coming from Japanese legends and traditional subjects, which he treats in a highly distinctive manner, often based upon flowing lines.
N53, N67, N85, N86, N94, N128, N216

Bokuzan 19th century. Believed to come from Nagoya, where he made small netsuke of shells, invariably in wood, his signature carved in the *ukibori* technique.
IN90

Bunsai There appear to be three artists listed using this name. The foremost among these was the lacquerer Koma Bunsai, the second son of Koma Kansai I. Alain Ducros, in his book *Netsuke et Sagemono* 1987, lists Shimizu Bunsai as a Meiji lacquerer; Ueda Reikichi mentions Tani Bunsai, with no details. No other piece bearing the seal signature appears to have been recorded.
N238

Chogetsu, Shunkosai 1826-1892. Lived in Edo/Tokyo and made *katabori* netsuke of various subjects, as well as *manju*, always in ivory or walrus tusk.
IN45, S58

Chohei, Nomura see **Index of Inro Artists**

Daieido, Hokuetsu No known details.
N126

Doraku 19th century. Was born in Onomichi but subsequently lived in Osaka where he worked in wood and ivory, his netsuke being of subjects used by other Osaka artists.
IN71

Dosho, Kagei 1828-1884. Lived in Osaka and was adept at carving netsuke in a variety of materials. His work was either naturalistic or stylised and his output included a number of fine *manju-*style netsuke.
N54, N137, N201, N220, N237

Eiraku A ceramicist from Kyoto who was succeeded by several generations using the same name.
N225

Ekizan Apparently unrecorded.
IN27

Gogetsu The netsuke attached to the inro cited below is the only recorded example.
IN 59

Gyokusen The signature on this example is in the *kanji* known to have been used by an 18th century artist from Kyoto although the work is evidently of the late Edo/ Meiji period, and of the style prevalent in Tokyo at the time.
N133, IN56

Gyokuso, Ouchi 1879-1944. Lived in Tokyo and studied under Miyasaki Joso before becoming independent.
He worked mainly in boxwood and ivory, his netsuke being always neat and well finished.
N77

Gyokuyosai Worked between about 1825 and 1870 in Edo/Tokyo. He made a variety of animal and figure netsuke, always in ivory, some with lacquered details.
N211

Gyokuzan see **Index of Inro Artists**

Hakuryu, Unsho Mid 19th century. Lived in Kyoto and worked mainly in ivory and occasionally in wood, his subjects ranging from animals of the zodiac in the Kyoto tradition, to simple studies of fruit similar to those produced by Ohara Mitsuhiro.
N244, N255

Hakuyosai see **Shoraku**

Harumitsu Late 19th century. Pupil of Suzuki Masanao II of Ise. He produced a number of netsuke, many of which are somewhat large and elaborate, negating their use and more akin to small *okimono*. His work, however, was very fine and invariably in lightly stained boxwood.
N99, S44

Hashi-ichi, Hashimoto see **Index of Sagemono Artists**

Hojitsu, Meikeisai 1790-1873. Lived in Tokyo and worked in ivory and wood, producing a large number of *katabori* netsuke and *manju*, sometimes with inlaid details.
IN70, IN73

Horaku 19th century. Lived in Kyoto and worked in ebony and boxwood, producing a number of fine netsuke of animals, particularly bats, as well as birds and groups of buildings.
N45, N235

Hozan, Tanaka Mid to late 19th century. He lived in Tokyo, was a pupil of Meikeisai Hojitsu and worked in wood and ivory.
N96

Ikkan 1817-1893. Lived in Nagoya and excelled in the carving of netsuke, invariably in wood. His subjects included zodiac and other animals, mythical and genre figures, always intricately carved in a life-like manner and highly finished.
N6

Ikko, Hasegawa Probably early to mid 19th century. There is much doubt as to where he lived and worked, various authorities citing Tsu, Tokyo, Kyoto and Osaka as his abode. He was a prodigious maker of *kiseruzutsu,* as well as inro and netsuke, the former often of various materials and with inlay.
N162, S45, S72

Ikko It is not certain which of the many artists of the name this is, although the work appears to be of the early 19th century.
S70

Ikkokusai see **Index of Sagemono Artists**

Ikkosai Late 18th/early 19th century. Believed to have come from Osaka, where he worked in wood, creating boldly rendered figural netsuke.
N139

Ikkosai see **Toun**

Ikku (Isamu Kasuya) was born in 1949 and studied under Saito Yasufusa. He produces finely detailed netsuke in variously stained ivory, partly dyed with *yasha* lacquer.
N66, N87

Issai 19th century. A lacquerer and carver, possibly of the same school as Shibata Zeshin and Taishin. A few *kagamibuta* and *hako*-netsuke are recorded bearing this name.
IN6

Issan, Ryusenshi An artist about whom little is known. Two pieces bearing the name Ryusenshi have been recorded, but this appears to be the only recorded example of the full name on a netsuke.
N39

Jobun Little is known about him, save that he was reputedly a pupil of Ryukei I of Edo (mistakenly referred to as Hokei I in Neil Davey's book, *Netsuke,* based on the M.T. Hindson collection).
N111

Jokasai, Yamada see **Index of Inro Artists**

Juei (Toshinaga), Kojima Late 19th century. Lived in Tokyo and was possibly a follower of Meikeisai Hojitsu.
IN89

Jugyoku, Ryukosai Early to mid 19th century. Worked in a variety of materials, producing *katabori* netsuke of animal and figure subjects as well as *manju,* often with inlaid details.
N83, N136

Kagetoshi Early 19th century. He is widely recorded as having lived in Kyoto, although Reikichi and Okada cite him as being domiciled in Nagoya. His work, mostly in ivory, is highly distinctive with a profusion of finely carved detail.
N192

Kaigyokusai see **Masatsugu**

Kajikawa (family) See **Index of Inro Artists**

Kanman 1793-1859. Lived in Kaai, in Iwami province and became a member of the circle of netsuke makers that started with Seiyodo Tomiharu. He made *katabori* netsuke in wood, as well as relief carvings on boars' tusks.
N269

Kansai, Koma see **Index of Inro Artists**

Kanshosai see **Index of Inro Artists**

Kenya 1825-1889. A ceramicist from Edo/Tokyo and a follower of Kenzan, who produced a number of netsuke as well as ceramic inlay on inro.
IN40

Kikuhiko No known details.
S79

Ko The single character *Ko* has been seen on a number of netsuke of similar type, carved and inlaid in a style associated with Ozaki Kokusai and his followers from Edo.
N18

Kodo, Okuda Born in 1940 and has produced a number of highly distinctive netsuke and *okimono.* He learnt the art of carving from his father but is also a gifted painter, for which work he uses the art name Masato Okuda. He also uses the art name Umaroku.
N78

Kogetsu Mid. 19th century. Worked almost entirely in wood, his subjects including tortoises, frogs, *kappa* and wasps in rotten pears, the model for which he is most renowned.
N101

Kokei Late 18th/early 19th century. He was apparently a pupil of, or was apprenticed to, Tanaka Minko of Tsu. He lived in Kuwana and produced many netsuke, mostly of animals, although some figural subjects are known. From the large number of works bearing his name that are recorded, one can deduce that he either had a large workshop with many apprentices or that he was copied during and after his lifetime.
N9, N12, N15, N28, N40, N43, N49, N69, IN37, IN38

Kokusai, Ozaki 1835-c.1892. Once believed by Western students to have lived in Asakusa, Tokyo, but now known to have lived and worked in Shitamachi, Tokyo. He excelled in the carving of netsuke in stag antler and ivory, generally of Chinese traditional subjects, often treating them with a touch of humour.
N37, N121, N152, IN34

Kokusai, Ozaki (attributed to).
N7

Komin Details unknown, but from the style, he lived in Edo during the middle part of the 19th century.
N182

Kosai, Suzuki Late 19th century. A follower of Meikeisai Hojitsu, he worked in Tokyo, mostly in ivory, making *manju* as well as *katabori* netsuke.
N114

Kozan, Toryusai 19th century. Lived in Iwashiro. He was very versatile, often working in wood, although he is perhaps best known for his highly detailed walnut carvings.
N2

Kozan 19th century. The artist is possibly Shohosai Kozan, probably from Iwami, who made lacquered netsuke in the Ritsuo revival manner.
IN26

Kyubei, Karamono 18th century. He lived in Sakai and made netsuke of moulded bronze, having studied the art of metalwork and particularly the bronze work of the Chinese Ming dynasty.
N254

Kyusai, Tetsugen(do) 1879-1938. Born in Osaka, he was adept at working in wood and ivory, producing netsuke mostly of relatively small size and carved with naturalistic detail.
N264

Masakiyo, Sakai Late 19th century. Lived in Uji, Yamada, and was a pupil of Suzuki Masakatsu, from whom he learnt the art of making netsuke in the tradition of the Masanao family of Ise.
N44

Masamitsu (Hagiwara Kaiko) 19th century. He was a clansman of the family of Tatebayashi Akimoto from Joshu, from where he travelled to Tokyo to study ivory carving under Kaneko Saito. He is distinguished from other carvers of the same name by the peculiar flourish with which he signed his name.
N265

Masanao (of Ise) There were several artists using this name, all working in Ise in Yamada province, from the early to later parts of the 19th century, producing wood netsuke of various subjects. It is virtually impossible to distinguish between them, although the first mentioned here is probably one of the earlier carvers, while the latter two were probably made by descendants.
N68, N74, N263

Masanao, Shinzan (style)1904-1982. A direct descendant of the Masanao family of Ise, Yamada, producing netsuke of the same subjects as his forebears. He learnt the art of carving from his father Sakai Masakiyo.
N25

Masatada Came from Kyoto and carved in the manner of Mitsuhide, with whom he was evidently associated.
N35

Masatomo There were several artists of this name. The present example was probably produced in Edo during the early 19th century.
N197

Masatsugu, Kaigyokusai 1818-1892. Lived in Osaka. He worked mainly in ivory and occasionally in wood and other materials. He was and is generally regarded by connoisseurs in Japan as the finest netsuke artist of the 19th century. His work in later life could sometimes be termed a little bland, but none could fault his technical expertise.
N1, N30, N36, N61, N127

Masayuki 19th century. The artist is probably Hoshunsai Masayuki, who lived in Tokyo and was associated with Ozaki Kokusai and Ishikawa Rensai.
IN15

Masayuki, Isshinsai 19th century. Believed to have lived in Osaka, making *manju* and other netsuke with relief carving.
N190

Minjo, Unno 1868-1910. Lived in Edo and made many *kanamono* and *kagamibuta* plates as well as sword fittings.
N172, IN24

Minko, Tanaka 1735-1816. Lived in Tsu, in Mie prefecture, where he made a large number of netsuke and *tonkotsu* in wood, sometimes with inlay. His work is bold and he had a number of apprentices who worked in the same manner. He was copied in his own lifetime and after his death.
N32, N145, N151, N168, N181, N262, IN37, IN62, S74, S78, S79, S85

Minkoku, Genryosai Late 18th/early 19th century. Lived in Edo, where he made mainly figural netsuke in wood, sometimes in the manner of Miwa. He was succeeded by his pupil Shuyusai Minkoku II.
N157

Mitsuhiro, Ohara 1810-1875. Lived in Osaka and made a wide variety of netsuke, mostly in ivory, although a few boxwood examples are known. His work was always highly finished and often stained. He was adept at *katakiri* work on *manju* and *ojime,* leading one to believe that he was also an accomplished painter.
N29, N55, N56, N57, N58, N75, N76, N84, N131, N149, N210, N229, N230, N248, N250, N258, N259, N260, IN21, S54, S55, S77

Mitsuhiro, Ohara (style).
N59

Mitsusada, Ohara 19th century. A contemporary of Ohara Mitsuhiro, living in Osaka and working in a similar style.
N245

Miwa There were a number of carvers using the name Miwa, all living in Edo, the first was recorded in *Soken Kisho* of 1781, while his successors produced netsuke well into the 19th century. They are all invariably of wood, many of ebony or fruitwood, and almost all of figural subjects, taken from legend or everyday life.
N180, N184, N208, IN72

Moritoshi, Kosai Mid to late 19th century. He worked in Edo, making a few *katabori* netsuke, but mainly *manju*, generally with legendary scenes carved in relief.
N138, N153, N165, N169

Nanka, Ichimuken 19th century. A maker of ivory *manju* and inro, which he engraved with maps of Japan and long inscriptions in fine *kebori*.
IN86

Nanka, Ichimuken (style).
N236

Naohiro Little is known of Naohiro, but from the style of the works recorded, he probably lived in Edo during the middle of the 19th century, making *katabori* netsuke and *manju* in ivory.
N161

Naoyuki see **Haritsu, Ogawa**

Norishige Little is known of this artist, who lived in Edo and produced a number of ivory netsuke, predominantly of single figures or groups, many with intricate detail.
N135

Okakoto Late 18th/early 19th century. Lived in Kyoto and worked mainly in ivory, making netsuke of real and imaginary animals, as well as human figures.
IN19

Okatomo (after) Late 18th century. He lived in Kyoto, producing mainly animal netsuke in ivory. The present example is in his style but was created somewhat later.
IN43

Raku Late 18th century. The single character signature has been seen on a few netsuke and it has been suggested that Raku and Risuke Garaku of Osaka were the same artist.
N251

Rakushi 19th century metalworker.
IN53

Rensai, Ishikawa Mid to late 19th century. Born in Shizuoka but moved to Edo where he made netsuke in stag-antler and ivory in the manner of Ozaki Kokusai.
N41

Rensai, Ishikawa (style).
N122

Rensha Little is known of this artist. Only three examples of his work have been recorded, all seemingly made during the first half of the 19th century.
N221

Ryokuzan Late 19th/early 20th century. Worked in ivory, making models of fruit and nuts, which he stained for effect. A similar example to the Atchley netsuke is illustrated in George Lazarnick, *NIA*, p. 883.
IN97

Ryukei, Shinshisai Early to mid. 19th century. Born in Kyoto but moved to Edo, where he carved figural netsuke in wood and ivory.
N154

Ryumin, Ono Late 19th century. He lived in Tokyo, working mainly in ivory, making figural netsuke and masks.
N195

Ryumin, Serisawa Late 19th century. He was a metalworker, a student of Tenmin, who made *kanamono (kanagu)* and *kagamibuta* plates.
N141, N231

Ryusenshi, see **Issan**

Sekisen Late 19th century. A ceramicist who made a large number of copies of *No* and other theatrical masks.
N193

Sensho No known details.
N105

Shaw, Guy 1957-2003. Lived in southern England and made a number of highly finished netsuke, using a variety of materials and was extremely innovative in his choice of subjects and the manner in which he treated them.
N71

Shibayama (family) A large family of artists known for their elaborate inlay, using a variety of materials. The style was founded by Onogi Senzo in the late 18th century, although the majority of known examples were produced during the latter part of the 19th century.
IN95

Shigemasa From the style, Shigemasa evidently emanated from Osaka, the staining of the ivory showing affinities with that used at certain times by Ohara Mitsuhiro and Anraku during the middle part of the 19th century.
N60

Shigetsu No known details.
N226

Shingetsu The art name of Fujio Muramatsu who was born in 1934 and, having studied with Kogyoku Muramatsu and Shinsho Kikuchi, became an independent artist in 1958.
N52

Shosai 20th century. Made netsuke for export in wood and ivory.
N215

Shoraku, Hakuyosai 19th century. A follower of the Kikugawa school of Edo/Tokyo.
N166

Shuji Early to mid 19th century. Carved in wood, producing netsuke of reptilian subjects.
S76

Shuzan, Yoshimura (style) Died 1776. He lived in Osaka and was a gifted painter and netsuke carver. His designs were taken from Chinese and Japanese art books and were often of soft wood with painted details. His work was widely copied both within and after his lifetime.
N117

Somin, Yokoya There were five metalworkers of this name living in Edo, the first died in 1691 and the fifth worked in the early 19th century. Each made sword fittings, and the later artists also made *kanagu* and *kagamibuta* plates. The family had a number of followers and it is difficult to distinguish between the work of each of the later makers.
N104

Sukeyuki Late 19th century. One of a group of carvers from Takayama in Hida province, producing *katabori* and *ittobori* netsuke and *okimono*.
N119

Tadachika, Toyosai Mid to late 19th century. Lived in Edo, where he worked entirely in ivory, making *katabori* netsuke, mainly of figures, as well as *manju*.
IN46

Tadashige From the style, this artist probably lived in Nagoya during the early to middle 19th century.
N205

Tadatoshi c.1770-1840. One of the foremost artists from Nagoya, working only in wood, producing small, neat netsuke, with fine detailed carving.
N73

Takusai, Tategawa (or Tachigawa) 1817-1888. A member of the Tategawa (Tachigawa) family of sculptors and netsuke carvers, working entirely in wood and making mainly figural and animal netsuke.
IN11

Tametaka 18th century. Mentioned in *Soken Kisho* and lived in Nagoya, where he made a number of fine wood netsuke, often of bold design and execution.
N202

Teiji Late 19th century. He was originally a potter and made ceramic netsuke as well as wood and lacquer examples on which he applied designs in glazed pottery.
IN29, S74

Tekkan Late 19th century. He was a student of Kano Tessai and made *kiseruzutsu* and mask netsuke, often with painted details.
N198

Tenmin There were two artists of this name, both metalworkers. The first was born in 1799 and made *kanagu*, *kagamibuta* and sword fittings. He was still working in 1870. The second was born in 1864 and was a student of Unno Shomin. His output was mainly for export. The Atchley example is probably by the former.
N142

Toen, Morikawa 1820-1894. Lived in Nara and produced a number of *sashi* style netsuke, similar to the present example, as copies of well-known treasures, at the behest of the Imperial Museum.
N106

Tokoku, Suzuki 1846-1913. Lived in Tokyo, where he is believed to have studied under Ozaki Kokusai and made netsuke and *kiseruzutsu* in his style, before leaving to become an independent artist, making netsuke in a variety of materials, often with coloured inlay.
IN54, S3, S5, S43

Tokoku (style).
N206, IN87

Tomin Early 19th century. A follower of Tanaka Minko, making netsuke very much in his master's style.
N194

Tomokazu, Kano Late 18th/early 19th century. Worked in wood and produced animal and figural netsuke, finished to a high standard. He was succeeded by at least two other carvers who adopted the same name.
N4, N38, N80, IN20

Tomomitsu One of the followers of Chikuyosai Tomochika, working in Edo during the last half of the 19th century.
N150

Tomonobu, Arima Early 19th century. Possibly worked in Nagoya and made groups of vegetables and shells, as well as animals and reptiles in wood.
N95

Tomotada, Izumiya 18th century. Lived in Kyoto and was mentioned in *Soken Kisho* of 1781. He worked in wood and ivory, his main output appearing to be animals of the zodiac.
N10

Tomotada, Izumiya (after)
N5, N8, N204

Tomotada The maker of this example may be Eirakusai Tomotada, described as living in Edo during the 19th century, making figural netsuke.
N178

Toshinaga see **Juei**

Toun, Ikkosai Mid. 19th century. Lived in Edo and produced a large number of figural and animal netsuke, almost always in ivory.
IN47, S84

Towne, Anthony Born 1956. Lives in Portland, Oregon, where he makes netsuke of walnut and fossilised walrus tusk.
N200

Umaroku see **Kodo, Okuda**

Yoshihiko see **Index of Sagemono Artists**

Yoshihisa Nothing is known of this artist, the Atchley netsuke being the only recorded example.
N183

Yoshikata Late 18th century. Worked in wood and made elegant figural netsuke.
N123

Yoshimichi (or Kodo) Nothing is known of this artist, the Atchley netsuke being the only recorded example.
N65

Yoshitomo 19th century. Two very similar examples are recorded, the other in the *Meinertzhagen Card Index,* p. 998. Another example, of a seated figure, is signed Heian (Kyoto) Yoshitomo.
N222

Yoshitomo No details known, although from the evidence of the present example, he probably worked in Edo during the middle part of the 19th century.
N160

Youngren, Lee Born 1918 in Minneapolis, Minnesota. Now lives in San Juan Capistrano, California, and creates netsuke in wood, stone, marble and plaster.
N31, N88

Yoyusai, Hara see **Index of Inro Artists**

Index of Inro artists

Ankyo see **Yasutada, Koma**

Bunryusai, Kajikawa There were three successive generations of the Kajikawa family as well as other lacquerers using this name. The first Bunryusai was the third master of the school and worked for the Shogunate in the late 17th century. The present examples are both from later generations.
IN48, IN49

Chikanaga, Fujiwara Nothing is known of the artist, this being apparently the only recorded example.
IN82

Chikanao, Ueda 18th century. Mentioned in *Soken Kisho*. His work was varied and with good designs, though the base and lacquer were somewhat weak, resulting in a number of chipped or otherwise damaged inro.
IN43

Chohei Late 18th/early 19th century. He lived in Edo and was appointed as lacquerer to the Shogun. His work features bold designs, often inlaid with *tsuishu*, *aogai* and *raden*.
IN22, IN29, IN30, S87

Gyokuzan, Jitokusai 19th century. Lived in Edo and made inro, ojime and *hako-netsuke* with a high degree of skill. He made lacquer wares that imitated other materials such as metal, and is known to have collaborated with the netsuke artist Suzuki Tokoku
IN31

Gyokuzan, Jitokusai (attributed)
IN61

Haritsu, Ogawa 1663-1747. Commonly known as Ritsuo, he was a painter, poet and ceramicist. He worked in a number of styles, and was adept at simulating various materials in lacquer. He also used a number of art names *(go),* including the name *Naoyuki* and the seal *Kan*. His inro and larger lacquered wares were often inlaid with metal or coloured pottery. He had a number of apprentices, whom he taught the techniques of his art, the foremost being Mochizuki Hanzan.
IN6, IN7, IN10, S53

Haritsu Ogawa (after).
IN39

Hashi-ichi see **Index of Sagemono Artists**

Ikki, Arakawa Died 1895. Lived in Tokyo and was well known as a maker of *kanagu* for *tabako-ire*.
IN94

Jokasai, Yamada A name used by a number of successive generations of lacquerers, the first, (Yamada Joka), working in Edo during the Kanbun era (1661-1673). The majority of the netsuke and inro seen bearing this name are of the late 18th and 19th centuries.
IN11, IN27, IN28, IN58, IN59, IN96

Josen (?) The artist is possibly that recorded by Wrangham in *The Index of Inro Artists,* p. 100. He worked in the early 19th century, producing wood inro with engraved designs.
IN68

Josen(sai) Late 18th/early 19th century. He was possibly associated with the Kajikawa family and produced many inro in a variety of techniques and styles.
IN67

Kajikawa (family) The most famous and most prolific family of lacquerers, who made many inro from the 17th century when the dynasty is said to have been founded by Kajikawa Hikobei. A number of other families and workshops were connected to the Kajikawa through the 18th and 19th centuries.
IN32, IN44, IN45, IN46, IN47, IN50

Kan see **Ogawa Haritsu**

Kansai, Koma There were three successive generations using the name Kansai. The first died in 1792 and the last in 1857. Each lived in Edo and was a highly skilled practitioner of the art. They were also masters of workshops, and included among their apprentices Bunsai and Shibata Zeshin.
IN5, IN23, IN39, IN64, N51

Kanshosai, see **Toju, Toshi** and **Toyo** see also **N247**

Kenya (attributed).
IN40

Kirei (?) Unknown.
IN72

Kisui Probably late 18th /early 19th century. A maker of Netsuke, this being the only inro recorded.
IN89

Kokei see **Index of Netsuke Artists**

Koma (family) The name of the most famous family of lacquerers, founded by Kyui in the 17th century and continuing through to the end of the 19th century. See also **Kansai, Koryu, Kyuhaku, Yasutada** and **Zeshin** in **Index of Inro Artists.**
IN91

Komin, Nakayama 1808-1870. Lived in Edo/Tokyo and learnt the art of lacquering from Hara Yoyusai. He was an accomplished and innovative lacquerer with a fine sense of design and was granted the title *Hokkyo* for his work.
IN60

Korin, Ogata (style) 1658-1715. Lived in Edo and was one of the foremost painters of the Rimpa school and a much lauded lacquerer. His signature appears on a number of inro, but it is believed by many that the engraved or lacquered name signifies the origin of the design rather than the maker.
IN41

Koryu, Koma Late 18th century. A fine lacquerer and maker of inro, who was succeeded by several generations and followers using the name.
IN64

Kyosui, Iwase 1816-1867. Worked in Kyoto as a painter and *ukiyo-e* book illustrator. He made inro and netsuke as well as using lacquer for his paintings *(urushi-e)*. He often used the paintings of others for his inro designs.
IN69

Kyuhaku, Koma There were at least six lacquerers from the Koma family using the name Kyuhaku. The first was lacquerer to the Shogunate and died in 1715. The sixth master died in 1816 and it is probably by him that the majority of inro thus signed were made. The name Yasuaki, seen on **IN22**, was a *go* used by Koma Kyuhaku II, who died in 1732.
IN20, IN21, IN22, IN62

Masanari, Shiomi 1647-1722. The son of Shiomi Harumasa and worked in Kyoto, where he excelled in the making of inro and other lacquer wares using the *togidashi* technique. He was followed by several generations using the same name well into the 19th century.
IN17, IN18, IN55, IN56

Masanari, Shiomi (style).
IN19

Muller, Armin 1932-2000. Lived in Santa Barbara, California, where he worked as a ceramicist and artist, together with his wife, Lynn Richardson. He developed the skill of producing ceramic inro, many of which were covered with a celadon glaze.
IN98, IN99

Nanka, Ichimuken See **index of Netsuke Artists**

Nemoto Late 19th/early 20th century. Worked in the Shibayama style, making inro and other gold lacquered wares, with profuse inlay of various materials.
IN95

Noriyuki, Hamano The artist who collaborated with Hara Yoyusai on the present example was probably Hamano Noriyuki II (1771-1852) or a follower, of whom there were many. The Hamano family was well known for their sword fittings, while later generations produced a number of *kanagu* and inro as well as metal inlay on inro by lacquerers.
IN70

Oyama 20th century. Known as a somewhat brash artist, who made a few inro with bold designs.
IN97

Reikaku No details known. Raymond Bushell lists an inro lacquered on polished wood, and the present example is the only other recorded.
IN88

Ritsuo see **Haritsu, Ogawa**

Seido (?) No details known.
IN71

Shigeyoshi, Hasegawa There were two generations of lacquerers using this name, the first working in Tsuyama during the late 18th century. Their work was generally fine and their designs often understated.
IN54

Shunsho, Yamamoto 1610-1682. Lacquerer, poet and calligrapher. He was a highly skilled maker of inro and larger lacquer wares, for which he was granted the title *Hokkyo*. He was succeeded by several generations, the last of whom was born in 1919. A number of seals were used by the family, the most common of which, first used by Shunsho II, was *Kagemasa*.
IN57

Shunsui, Ganshosai Late 19th/early 20th century. A fine lacquerer who worked in many diverse styles. His designs included traditional subjects, sometimes treated in a somewhat modernist manner.
IN96

Soetsu, Tsuchida (style) c. 1660-1745. Worked in Kyoto and Edo, producing inro and other lacquer wares with Rimpa style designs, his inro sometimes inscribed with the originator of the design. He was copied in his lifetime and after.
IN8

Somada (family) By repute, the family of lacquerers was founded by Somada Kiyosuke in the early 18th century. Their inro and other wares are typified by intricate designs, often influenced by Chinese paintings, in iridescent *aogai* and *raden,* augmented by details of gold and silver foil, generally on a polished black ground.
IN80

Sotetsu, Nakamura The Sotetsu family of lacquerers was founded in the 17th century by Yuzan of Kyoto (1617-1695) and successive generations worked through to the middle of the 19th century.
IN5

Takanori, Tatsuke 1757-1833 (?). A celebrated member of the Tatsuke family of lacquerers, who produced inro and netsuke, often taking his designs from those of Kano school painters.
IN32

Tatsuei, Shoryusai Late 18th/early 19th century. A lacquerer who specialised in *takamakie* but also occasionally produced pieces lacquered in *togidashi*. He used designs derived from Kano school artists and was granted the titles *Hogen* and *Hoin* for his work.
IN42

Togi Probably late 18th century. A competent lacquerer, by whom several examples are known, although details of his life and work are scarce.
IN34

Toju, Kanshosai Late 18th/early 19th century. Student of Iizuka Toyo and a versatile lacquerer who was apparently adept in a wide variety of techniques.
IN52, IN53

Tomohide, Kajikawa Late 18th century. A prolific member of the Kajikawa family, who used designs taken from various Kano school painters.
IN31

Toshi, Kanshosai Early 19th century. A fine lacquerer, who adopted the name Iizuka Toyo III and made a number of inro and netsuke lacquered in a variety of techniques and styles.
IN33

Toyo, Iizuka, Kanshosai. Late 18th century. A prodigious lacquerer, he also employed a number of apprentices who became fine workers in their own right (see **Toju, Toshi** above). He was employed by the *daimyo* of Awa, Shikoku, where he achieved the status of a *samurai*. He was adept in many techniques, and is particularly known for his *sumie togidashi* designs on *rogin-nuri* grounds.
IN51

Yasuaki see **Kyuhaku, Koma**

Yasuchika, Tsuchiya II 1697-1747 A member of the Tsuchiya family of metalworkers, living in Edo and best known for their sword fittings, although a few inro and *kanagu* are known.
IN24

Yasutada, Koma (alternative reading **Ankyo**) The name was an art name for Koma Kyuhaku I (died 1715), although very few, if any, of the inro bearing this name were produced prior to the end of the 18th century. He worked for a *daimyo* of Gifu for a while and was commissioned to make a set of one hundred inro for the *shogun,* featuring a different bird with associated plants. Other designs were taken from those of Kano school painters and *ukiyo-e* artists.
IN63

Yoyusai, Hara 1772-1845. Lived in Edo and worked for Lord Matsudaira. He had many apprentices who produced a large number of finely lacquered inro and other wares, often with his signature. Like other lacquerers, he used the designs of Rimpa painters, including Sakai Hoitsu.
IN18, IN70

Zeshin, Shibata 1807-1891. A consummate lacquerer, painter and wood-block print designer who lived in Edo, studied in Kyoto and produced a large number of inro and other wares with a distinctive style and with many innovative techniques. He learnt the art of lacquering from Koma Kansai I and that of painting from Suzuki Nanrei, Okamoto Toyohiko and Tani Buncho. He had several pupils, including his sons Reisai, Shinsai and Ryushin, although his most celebrated follower was Ikeda Taishin.
IN65, IN66

Zonsei 19th century. It is uncertain where he lived, although Shonai and Izumi are suggested by different scholars. He was highly adept in the art of *tsuishu* and *tsuikoku* lacquering, often carved with designs after Chinese mythology.
IN81

Index of *Sagemono* artists

Akiyuki, Naniwa (?) 19th century. Apparently otherwise unrecorded, although he appeared to live in Osaka (Naniwa).
S13

Baiun 19th century. Details unknown, except that Raymond Bushell has recorded the name on a *tsuishu* pipe-case.
S25

Bokko, Ando Late 19th/early 20th century. Pupil of Kano Tessai, who taught at the Tokyo Art School. A fine carver, who appeared to specialise in designs engraved in delicate *kebori* and *katakiri-bori*.
S57

Bokkoku Late 19th/early 20th century. A contemporary of Bokko, who was a carver and lacquerer, sometimes working with artists in other media to produce pipe-cases of *muso-zutsu* form.
S14, S24

Bunkido see **Shunzo**

Chogetsu, Shunkosai see **Index of Netsuke Artists**

Chohei see **Index of Inro Artists**

Doko The only reference to the name yet found is that on a wood netsuke, illustrated in George Lazarnick, *NIA*, p. 355.
S64

Ganbun, Jikan Early to mid 19th century. Lived in Edo and worked in horn, bamboo, wood and other materials, making netsuke, *kiseruzutsu, tonkotsu,* inro and other accoutrements. He specialised in the making of minute metal ants and other creatures, which he sometimes added to other carvers' netsuke.
S46

Harumitsu see **Index of Netsuke Artists**

Hashi-ichi (Hashimoto Ichizo) 1817-1882. Lived in Edo/Tokyo and started by producing sword scabbards but after 1876 made a number of varied lacquer wares, including netsuke. He is best known for the technique of simulating bamboo in lacquer with great accuracy. His apprentice and adopted son, Hasimoto Hashiichi II (1856-1924) continued in his master's style, becoming a professor at the Tokyo Art School.
S22, S23, N261, IN67

Heidai, Shoko The name is apparently unrecorded.
S71

Hekimen The only reference to this name, about which there are no known details, is that in Raymond Bushell, *The Inro Handbook*, p. 184.
S70

Hokei, Matsuki Late 19th century. Worked in Tokyo and became a professor in the Tokyo Art School in 1887. He specialised in the *tsuishu* technique of lacquering, his designs sometimes based upon Chinese mythology.
S26

Hokusen, Kitagawa 1846-1922. Lived in Mito and made some sword fittings as well as *mae-kanagu.*
S66

Homin, Iwagami Late 19th century. Maker of *okimono* and pipe-cases, whose work was generally very fine. He was mentioned in the list of ivory carvers working in Tokyo in 1886.
S11, S12

Ikko, Hasegawa see **Index of Netsuke Artists**

Ikkosai, see **Somin**

Ikkokusai There were seven successive generations of lacquerers using this name, the first (Kinjo, 1777-1851) having been employed by the Lord of Owari and the last being born in 1965.
S73, N100

Ippo, Yanigasawa A 19th century. A lacquerer, known for his pipe-cases as well as other lacquered objects, including combs and hairpins, as well as a green-lacquered *kodansu.*
S65

Kaiseki Late 19th century. No details known.
S16

Kan see **Haritsu, Ogawa**, **Index of Inro Artists**

Keishin Late 19th/early 20th century. Probably a student of Shibata Zeshin and contemporary of Ikeda Taishin. His works appear to be very rare.
S21

Kikuhiko see **Index of Netsuke Artists**

Kosai Late 19th century. Believed to be a student of Shibata Zeshin. A number of pipe-cases as well as netsuke bearing this signature have been recorded.
S31

Koshin, Maeyama Worked in the Meiji/Taisho periods (1868-1926) and used the seal Rosetsu. He made a variety of lacquered objects and was possibly associated with Shibata Zeshin or at least influenced by him.
S14

Kyo Nothing appears to be known of this maker, who signed with a simple seal in relief. Three examples have been recorded, in ivory, walrus tusk and stag-antler, all simulating bamboo.
S6

Masahide, Kurokawa 19th century. He excelled in the carving of netsuke formed of nuts and coconuts, as well as mask netsuke and a few *tonkotsu*. The name Kiyo engraved on several pieces, including the Atchley *tonkotsu*, refers to the town of Nagasaki.
S85

Masateru, Kaigyokudo Late 19th century. He lived Osaka and was the son of Masachika and grandson of Kaigyokusai Masatsugu. He produced a number of netsuke, *tonkotsu* and *kiseruzutsu*, mostly in boxwood.
S51

Minko, Tanaka see **Index of Netsuke Artists**

Mitsuharu, Mizuno Died 1895. Maker of word fittings as well as *kanagu* and *kagamibuta* plates.
S63

Mitsuhiro, Ohara see **Index of Netsuke Artists**

Moei (or **Shigenaga), Nakaoji** Late 18th/early 19th century. Generally known for his inro, often lacquered in fine gold and coloured *togidashi*. As with other lacquerers, he was followed by several successors who adopted the same name.
S20

Moriyoshi, Kobayashi Died c. 1900-1920. Made small sword fittings, including *kozuka* and *menuki*, as well as *kanagu* for *tabako-ire*.
S61

Myochin Family of armourers, the later generations of which made decorative objects of iron.
S84

Nobuyuki The artist is apparently unrecorded, save for a netsuke bearing the signature illustrated in George Lazarnick, *NIA*, p. 838.
S15

Norinaga Late 19th/early 20th century. Made sword fittings and *kanagu*.
S59

Onpo No details known.
S72

Rosetsu see **Koshin**

Sadatoshi Late 19th century. Made sword fittings as well as *kanagu*.
S62

Seiko Late 19th century.
S37

Shigenaga see **Moei**

Shiko No details known.
S7

Shiryu (or Yukitaka) No details known of this maker, although the style shown on the present example leads one to suppose that he may have been an *okimono* maker, working in the late 19th century.
S8

Shogyoku Late 19th century. Little is known of this maker but, from the examples recorded, he specialised in the inlay of ivory and wood on wood or woven pipe cases.
S32

Shokyo No details known, but he evidently worked in the late 19th century.
S35

Shunko Probably Hasegawa Shunko, a maker of sword fittings and *kanagu* as well as metal objects for the tea ceremony.
S62

Shunzo, Bunkido 1808-1885. He lived in Takamatsu and was the brother of Tamakichi Zokoku. He specialised in *tsuishu* and *tsuikoku* lacquering and founded a workshop which still exists in Kagawa prefecture.
S39

Somin, Ikkosai Late 19th/early 20th century. Maker of *okimono* and somewhat elaborate netsuke. Stated by Meinertzhagen to be a member of the Okawa (Ogawa) school.
S2

Taisai Late 19th/early 20th century. A lacquerer who was a contemporary of Ikeda Taishin and follower of Shibata Zeshin. A number of *hako*-netsuke and *manju* as well as pipe-cases have been recorded.
S19

Taishin, Ikeda 1825-1903. The most successful pupil of Shibata Zeshin who became a celebrated lacquerer, often working in the style of his master. He produced small and large boxes, inro and netsuke as well as pipe-cases.
S62

Taishin, Takagi 20th century. He worked in Chiba prefecture and produced a number of lacquered stands, vases and netsuke.
S61

Teiji see **Index of Netsuke Artists**

Tessai, Kano 1845-1925. A painter, sculptor and maker of netsuke, pipe-cases and *tonkotsu,* mostly of wood and bamboo, in which he was able to simulate various materials. He had a large number of students and followers and became a professor at the Tokyo Art School in 1890.
S36, S63

Tetsuo Late 19th century. A fine metalworker, who produced sword fittings and *kanagu* for pouches.
S56

Tokoku, Suzuki see **Index of Netsuke Artists**

Tomoaki Late 19th century. Lived in Tokyo and was a maker of netsuke and pipe-cases, as well as *okimono*.
S55

Tosen Late 19th century. A lacquerer who collaborated with Taisai on the Atchley pipe-case and with the netsuke maker Meizan.
S19

Yoshihiko, Suzuki 1884-1969. Lived in Tokyo and was a fine maker of sword fittings and other metal objects, including *kanagu* for *tabako-ire.*
S61, IN65

Yukitaka see **Shiryu**

Yuraku No known details.
S59

Publications Mentioned in Text

Raymond Bushell, *Collectors' Netsuke* (Walker/Weatherhill publishers, Tokyo and New York, 1971)

Raymond Bushell, *Netsuke Familiar and Unfamiliar: New Principles for Collecting,* (Weatherhill publishers, New York, 1975)

Raymond Bushell, *The Inro Handbook: Studies of Netsuke, Inro and Lacquer* (Weatherhill publishers, New York, 1979)

Sharen Chappell and Matthew Welch, *Netsuke: The Japanese Art of Miniature Carving,* catalogue of the exhibition held at the Minneapolis Institute of Arts, April–July, 1998, (published by Paragon Publishing)

Neil K. Davey, *Netsuke, A Comprehensive Study Based on the M. T. Hindson Collection,* (Sotheby Parke Bernet Publications, London, 1974; revised edition published by Philip Wilson publishers, 1982)

Alain Ducros, *Netsuke et Sagemono,* (Paris, 1987)

Eskenazi, Ltd., *The Charles A. Greenfield Collection of Inro and Lacquer,* catalogue of the exhibition. (London, 1990)

Robert E. Haynes, *The Index of Japanese Sword Fittings and Related Artists,* Nihon Art Publishers, Ellwangen, Germany, 2001

Bernard Hurtig, *Masterpieces of Netsuke Art: One Thousand Favorites of Leading Collectors* (Weatherhill Publishers, Tokyo and New York, 1973)

INCS, *Journal of the International Netsuke Collectors' Society* (Honolulu, Hawaii, 1973–1985)

INSJ, *the International Netsuke Society Journal (International Netsuke Society,* USA, 1996–present)

Japanese Lacquer from Southern California Collections. catalogue of the exhibition held at the Pacific Asia Museum, Pasadena, California, 1991.

H. L. Joly, *Legend in Japanese Art* (Kegan Paul, Trench and Trubner, London, 1908; reprinted, Charles E. Tuttle, Rutland, Vermont; Tokyo Japan, 1967)

H. L. Joly and K. Tomita, *Japanese Art and Handicraft.* catalogue of the loan exhibition held in aid of the British Red Cross, London, October-November 1915

Miriam Kinsey, *Living Masters of Netsuke* (Kodansha International, Tokyo, Japan; New York, NY, 1984)

Joseph Kurstin, M.D. and Maria L. Ortega, *Masterworks of Netsuke and Other Japanese Miniature Art from American Collections* (Lowe Art Museum, Miami, Florida, 1986)

George Lazarnick, *The Signature Book of Netsuke, Inro and Ojime Artists in Photographs* (Reed publishers, Honolulu, Hawaii, 1976)

George Lazarnick, *NIA, Netsuke and Inro Artists and How to Read Their Signatures* (Reed Publishers, Honolulu, Hawaii, 1982)

George Lazarnick, *MCI,* see also under Meinertzhagen

Frederick Meinertzhagen, *The Meinertzhagen Card Index at The British Museum,* edited by George Lazarnick (Alan R. Liss, inc., New York, 1986)

Paul Moss, *A Few More Early Link Tokokus,* INSJ, vol. 4, no.1, p.33

Paul Moss, *Bokko, Bokkoku, Bokuboku,* INSJ, vol. 22, no. 4, pp. 18-44

S. L. Moss: *Zodiac Beasts and Distant Cousins: Japanese Netsuke for Connoisseurs,* catalogue of the exhibition. (London, 1993)

S. L. Moss, *Netsuke: Serious Art, Outstanding Works Selected From American Collections,* catalogue of the exhibition. (London, 1989)

S. L. Moss, *Eccentrics in Netsuke,* catalogue of the exhibition. (London, 1982)

NK: *Netsuke Kenkyukai Journal,* (Netsuke Kenkyukai Society, USA, 1980-1996)

Barbra Teri Okada and Mary Gardner Neill, *Real and Imaginary Beings: The Netsuke Collection of Joseph and Edith Kurstin* (Yale University Art Gallery, 1980)

William and Betty Parker, *The Japanese Personal Smoking Set,* Arts of Asia, March/April, 1983

Andrew J. Pekarick, *Japanese Lacquer, 1600–1900.* catalogue of the exhibition, (Metropolitan Museum of Art, New York, 1980)

Harold P. Stern, , *The Magnificent Three, Lacquer, Netsuke and Tsuba.* catalogue of the Exhibition *Selections from the Collection of Charles A Greenfield,* (Japan House Gallery, New York, 1972)

Beatrice von Rague, *Iizuka Toyo, Orients Extramus,* pp. 163–235, Hamburg, 1964

Edward Wrangham, *The Index of Inro Artists,* (Harehope Publications, Alnwick, Northumberland, England, 1995)

V. F. Weber, *Koji Hoten: Dictionnaire, a l'Usage des Amateurs et Collectioneurs d'Objets d'Art Japonais et Chinois* (Paris, France, 1923; reprinted by Hacker Books, New York, 1965)

Masayoshi Yamada, *Gendai Netsuke (Netsuke: Modern Masterpieces)* (Nichibo Shuppan, Tokyo, 1989)

Exhibitions

October-November 1915. *Japanese Art and Handicraft,* a loan exhibition held in aid of the British Red Cross

New York, 1972. *The Magnificent Three, Lacquer, Netsuke and Tsuba*, Selections from the Collection of Charles A Greenfield, Japan House Gallery

Honolulu, 1975. An exhibition held on the occasion of the INCS convention.

Honolulu, 1977. An exhibition held on the occasion of the INCS convention.

Kansas City, Sept-Nov, 1977. An exhibition held on the occasion of the netsuke Kenkyukai convention at the William Rockhill Nelson Gallery, Atkins Museum

Los Angeles, Nov 1977-February 1978. *Beauty and The Beast – The Animal in Art,* Natural History Museum of Los Angeles County.

Minneapolis, September-October 1979. An exhibition held on the occasion of the Netsuke Kenkyukai convention.

Honolulu, 1983. An exhibition held on the occasion of the INCS convention.

New York, 1980 *Japanese Lacquer, 1600-1900*, Selections from the Charles A Greenfield collection, Metropolitan Museum of Art

London, 1980. *Contrasting Styles,* An exhibition held on the occasion of the London Netsuke Committee convention

Miami,1986. *Masterworks of Netsuke and Other Japanese Miniature Art from American Collections,* Lowe Art Museum

London, 1990. *The Charles A Greenfield Collection of Japanese Lacquer,* Eskenazi Ltd.

Pasadena California, 1991. *Japanese Lacquer From Southern California Collections*, Pacific Asia Museum.

Minneapolis, April-July 1998. *Netsuke, The Japanese Art of Miniature Carving*, Minneapolis Institute of Art.